TEACHER'S GUIDE
Workbook

Science

PEARSON
Scott
Foresman

Editorial Offices: Glenview, Illinois • Parsippany, New Jersey • New York, New York
Sales Offices: Needham, Massachusetts • Duluth, Georgia • Glenview, Illinois
Coppell, Texas • Sacramento, California • Mesa, Arizona

www.sfsuccessnet.com

Series Authors

Dr. Timothy Cooney
*Professor of Earth Science and
Science Education*
University of Northern Iowa (UNI)
Cedar Falls, Iowa

Dr. Jim Cummins
Professor
Department of Curriculum,
Teaching, and Learning
The University of Toronto
Toronto, Canada

Dr. James Flood
*Distinguished Professor of Literacy
and Language*
School of Teacher Education
San Diego State University
San Diego, California

Barbara Kay Foots, M.Ed.
Science Education Consultant
Houston, Texas

Dr. M. Jenice Goldston
*Associate Professor of Science
Education*
Department of Elementary Education
Programs
University of Alabama
Tuscaloosa, Alabama

Dr. Shirley Gholston Key
*Associate Professor of Science
Education*
Instruction and Curriculum Leadership
Department
College of Education
University of Memphis
Memphis, Tennessee

Dr. Diane Lapp
*Distinguished Professor of Reading
and Language Arts in Teacher
Education*
San Diego State University
San Diego, California

Sheryl A. Mercier
Classroom Teacher
Dunlap Elementary School
Dunlap, California

Dr. Karen L. Ostlund
UTeach, College of Natural Sciences
The University of Texas at Austin
Austin, Texas

Dr. Nancy Romance
*Professor of Science Education
& Principal Investigator*
NSF/IERI Science IDEAS Project
Charles E. Schmidt College
of Science
Florida Atlantic University
Boca Raton, Florida

Dr. William Tate
*Chair and Professor of Education
and Applied Statistics*
Department of Education
Washington University
St. Louis, Missouri

Dr. Kathryn C. Thornton
Professor
School of Engineering and
Applied Science
University of Virginia
Charlottesville, Virginia

Dr. Leon Ukens
Professor of Science Education
Department of Physics, Astronomy,
and Geosciences
Towson University
Towson, Maryland

Steve Weinberg
Consultant
Connecticut Center for
Advanced Technology
East Hartford, Connecticut

Consulting Author

Dr. Michael P. Klentschy
Superintendent
El Centro Elementary School District
El Centro, California

ISBN: 0-328-12606-3

ISBN: 0-328-20072-7

Copyright © Pearson Education, Inc.

3 4 5 6 7 8 9 10 V084 13 12 11 10 09 08 07 06 05

© Pearson Education, Inc.

Unit A
Life Science

Unit B
Earth Science

Unit C
Physical Science

Unit D
Space and Technology

Name _____

What does the bold word in each sentence mean?
Circle the letter of the best answer.

1. The **deciduous** trees were bare by December 1.
   A. dead or dying
   B. shedding leaves every year

2. **Seedlings** had sprouted from the seeds we planted.
   A. new leaves
   B. small, new plants

3. Bees often **pollinate** flowers as they fly from plant to plant.
   A. move pollen to seed-making part
   B. remove pollen to make seeds

4. A pine tree is an example of a **coniferous** tree.
   A. describes trees that grow cones to make seeds
   B. describes plants with a strong scent

5. Seeds can **germinate** if they have the right amounts of water, light, and air.
   A. live a long time
   B. start to grow

6. A new plant gets food from its **seed leaf** at first.
   A. green part of a seed
   B. part of a seed that has food

7. We can learn about plants of the past by looking at **fossils**.
   A. marks left in rock
   B. plants no longer alive

8. The root **system** of a plant takes in water and minerals and holds the plant in place.
   A. small parts
   B. parts that work together

9. Many plants that once grew on Earth are now **extinct**.
   A. smaller
   B. no longer alive

Notes for Home: Your child learned the vocabulary terms for Chapter 1.
Home Activity: Ask your child to show you illustrations in the book that help him or her understand the vocabulary terms. Use the words in sentences as you talk about the pictures.

🎯 Compare and Contrast

Read the paragraph.

Trees and Grasses

Trees and grasses are both plants. They both have leaves and root systems. Both need sunshine, water, and minerals. However, grasses are small, with soft stems and fine roots. Trees are large, with wood stems and large, deep roots.

Apply It!

How are trees and grasses the same and different? Use the information from the science article to fill in the graphic organizer on page 3.

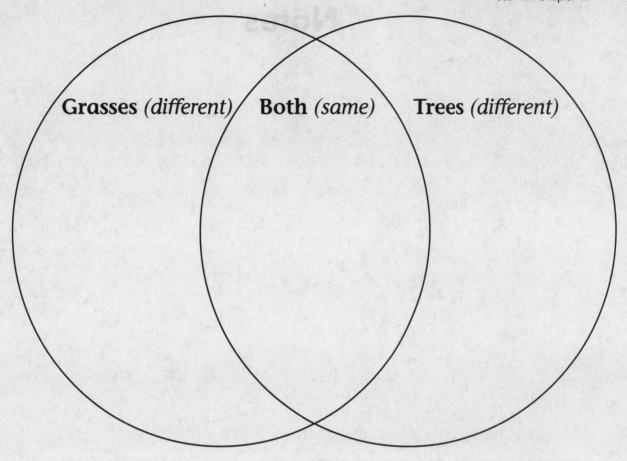

Grasses *(different)* **Both** *(same)* **Trees** *(different)*

Notes for Home: Your child has learned how to compare and contrast living things.
Home Activity: Read the information on two different seed packets with your child. Discuss how the plants are the same and different in their growing requirements and habits.

Notes

Lesson 1: What are the main parts of a plant?

Before You Read Lesson 1

Read each statement below. Place a check mark in the circle to indicate whether you agree or disagree with the statement.

	Agree	Disagree
1. Roots take in food for plants.	○	○
2. Leaves make sugar and oxygen for plants.	○	○
3. Plants release water through leaves.	○	○

After You Read Lesson 1

Reread each statement above. If the lesson supports your choice, place a check mark in the *Correct* circle. Then explain how the text supports your choice. If the lesson does not support your choice, place a check mark in the *Incorrect* circle. Then explain why your choice is wrong.

	Correct	Incorrect
1. _____	○	○
2. _____	○	○
_____		
3. _____	○	○
_____		

Notes for Home: Your child has completed a pre/post inventory of key concepts in the lesson.
Home Activity: Have your child compare different types of leaves on plants in and around your home. Together look at leaf parts through a magnifying glass.

Reviewing Terms: Sentence Completion

Complete the sentence with the correct word or phrase.

_____ 1. A plant's leaves are one kind of _____ because they have parts that work together. (shelter, system)

Reviewing Concepts: True or False

Write **T** (True) or **F** (False) on the line before each statement.

_____ 2. All living things need air and water.

_____ 3. Both plants and animals can make their own food.

_____ 4. The main parts of a plant are the roots, stems, leaves, and oxygen.

_____ 5. Plants use energy from the soil to make food.

_____ 6. Sugar and oxygen are made in leaves.

_____ 7. Some leaves protect plants from being eaten by hungry animals.

_____ 8. Leaves help plants in more than one way.

Applying Strategies: Measurement

Use complete sentences to answer question 9. (2 points)

9. Leaves come in many shapes and sizes. What tool would you use to measure the length of a leaf? Explain your choice.

_____

_____

_____

_____

Lesson 2: Why do plants need roots and stems?

Before You Read Lesson 2

Read each statement below. Place a check mark in the circle to indicate whether you agree or disagree with the statement.

	Agree	Disagree
1. Roots can store food for plants.	○	○
2. Plant stems are like two-way pipelines.	○	○
3. People eat roots and stems.	○	○

After You Read Lesson 2

Reread each statement above. If the lesson supports your choice, place a check mark in the *Correct* circle. Then explain how the text supports your choice. If the lesson does not support your choice, place a check mark in the *Incorrect* circle. Then explain why your choice is wrong.

	Correct	Incorrect
1. _____	○	○
_____		
2. _____	○	○
_____		
3. _____	○	○
_____		

Notes for Home: Your child has completed a pre/post inventory of key concepts in the lesson.
Home Activity: Together with your child, look at vegetables in your kitchen. Have your child identify which are leaves, which are roots, and which are stems.

Reviewing Concepts: Matching

Match each description with the correct word or phrase. Write the letter on the line next to each description.

_____ 1. where most plant root systems are found

_____ 2. the materials taken in by roots

_____ 3. these carry water and are found in roots and stems

_____ 4. large roots that grow deep in the ground

_____ 5. found on the outside of a cactus stem

_____ 6. parts of stems that protect plants from animals

_____ 7. stems that are thin and grow along the ground

_____ 8. these are held up by a plant's stem

a. tubes
b. below the ground
c. water and minerals
d. leaves, flowers, and fruits
e. taproots
f. thorns and stinging hairs
g. stolons
h. thick, waxy covering

Writing

Use complete sentences to answer question 9. (2 points)

9. Name two ways a plant's stem system can help a plant to survive in its environment.

_____

_____

_____

_____

© Pearson Education, Inc.

Lesson 3: How are plants grouped?

Before You Read Lesson 3

Read each statement below. Place a check mark in the circle to indicate whether you agree or disagree with the statement.

	Agree	Disagree
1. Trees are flowering plants.	○	○
2. Deciduous trees keep their leaves.	○	○
3. Wind can pollinate a flower.	○	○

After You Read Lesson 3

Reread each statement above. If the lesson supports your choice, place a check mark in the *Correct* circle. Then explain how the text supports your choice. If the lesson does not support your choice, place a check mark in the *Incorrect* circle. Then explain why your choice is wrong.

	Correct	Incorrect
1. _____	○	○
_____		
2. _____	○	○
_____		
3. _____	○	○
_____		

Notes for Home: Your child has completed a pre/post inventory of key concepts in the lesson.
Home Activity: Go for a walk with your child in your neighborhood or in a park. Ask your child to identify a deciduous tree, an evergreen, and a grass.

© Pearson Education, Inc.

Reviewing Terms: Matching

Match each definition with the correct word. Write the letter on the line next to each definition.

_____ 1. trees that lose their leaves in the fall   **a.** coniferous

_____ 2. trees that grow cones to make seeds   **b.** deciduous

_____ 3. to move pollen so a seed can form   **c.** pollinate

Reviewing Concepts: Sentence Completion

Complete each sentence with the correct word or phrase.

_____ 4. _____ are flowering plants that grow back from the roots each spring. (Grasses, Trees)

_____ 5. The function of a flower is to make _____. (cones, seeds)

_____ 6. In order for a seed to form, _____ must be moved from one part of a flower to another. (needles, pollen)

_____ 7. The seeds of deciduous trees form in _____. (flowers, cones)

_____ 8. Fruits form on some _____ plants. (coniferous, flowering)

Applying Strategies: Compare and Contrast

Use complete sentences to answer question 9. (2 points)

9. Describe one way in which seed cones and pollen cones are similar. Then describe one difference between them.

_____

_____

_____

Lesson 4: How do new plants grow?

Before You Read Lesson 4

Read each statement below. Place a check mark in the circle to indicate whether you agree or disagree with the statement.

	Agree	Disagree
1. The seedling protects the seed.	○	○
2. The seed leaf becomes a new plant.	○	○
3. Sticky seeds are spread by animals.	○	○

After You Read Lesson 4

Reread each statement above. If the lesson supports your choice, place a check mark in the *Correct* circle. Then explain how the text supports your choice. If the lesson does not support your choice, place a check mark in the *Incorrect* circle. Then explain why your choice is wrong.

	Correct	Incorrect
1. _____	○	○
_____		
2. _____	○	○
_____		
3. _____	○	○
_____		

Notes for Home: Your child has completed a pre/post inventory of key concepts in the lesson.
Home Activity: Gather different kinds of seeds from packets, fruit, or the outdoors. Ask your child how he or she thinks each seed is spread.

© Pearson Education, Inc.

Name _____

Reviewing Terms: Sentence Completion

Complete each sentence with the correct word or phrase.

_____ 1. A seed can _____, or start to grow, when the conditions are right. (scatter, germinate)

_____ 2. A new plant uses food stored in the _____. (seed leaf, seedling)

_____ 3. A _____ is a plant that has just germinated. (seedling, flower)

Reviewing Concepts: True or False

Write **T** (True) or **F** (False) on the line before each statement.

_____ 4. Some seeds are scattered by animals.

_____ 5. A seed can germinate no matter what the temperature is.

_____ 6. Coconuts are seeds that are scattered by the wind.

_____ 7. Seeds are protected by a seed coat.

_____ 8. All seeds are scattered in the same way.

Applying Strategies: Bar Graphs

9. Kendra planted seeds. She counted how many seeds germinated each day. Make a bar graph that shows Kendra's data. (2 points)

_____

_____

_____

Day	Number of Seeds Germinating
Monday	5
Tuesday	3
Wednesday	2

© Pearson Education, Inc.

Workbook

Lesson 5: How are plants from the past like today's plants?

Before You Read Lesson 5

Read each statement below. Place a check mark in the circle to indicate whether you agree or disagree with the statement.

	Agree	Disagree
1. The first plants had no flowers or seeds.	O	O
2. Living plants are exactly like extinct plants.	O	O
3. A petrified fossil is made of rock.	O	O

After You Read Lesson 5

Reread each statement above. If the lesson supports your choice, place a check mark in the *Correct* circle. Then explain how the text supports your choice. If the lesson does not support your choice, place a check mark in the *Incorrect* circle. Then explain why your choice is wrong.

	Correct	Incorrect
1. _____	O	O
_____		
2. _____	O	O
_____		
3. _____	O	O
_____		

 Notes for Home: Your child has completed a pre/post inventory of key concepts in the lesson.
Home Activity: Have your child compare a picture of a fern to the fossils of ferns shown on text page 22. Talk about ways they look the same and different.

Reviewing Terms: Matching

Match each definition with the correct word. Write the letter on the line next to each definition.

_____ 1. the remains or mark of a living thing from long ago

_____ 2. kinds of plants that are no longer alive anywhere on Earth

a. extinct
b. fossil

Reviewing Concepts: True or False

Write **T** (True) or **F** (False) on the line before each statement.

_____ 3. Fossils do not show anything about the kinds of plants that lived long ago.

_____ 4. Fossils form when rock replaces the parts of a plant.

_____ 5. Fossils form over a short period of time.

_____ 6. Some plant fossils are imprints.

_____ 7. Extinct plants are growing on Earth today.

_____ 8. Some plants alive today are similar to ancient ones.

Applying Strategies: Sequencing

Use complete sentences to answer question 9. (2 points)

9. Using the clue words in the sentences below, write the steps of fossil formation in the correct order.

Next, the plant was pressed in the mud.
Finally, the mud hardened into rock.
First, the plant died.
Then the plant rotted away.

_____

_____

_____

Elapsed Time

Jim will take care of the garden in July. The plants in the garden need to be watered every three days. They need to be weeded every seven days.

July						
				1 Weed water	2	3
4	5	6	7	8	9	10
11	12	13	14	15	16	17
18	19	20	21	22	23	24
25	26	27	28	29	30	31

1. Jim weeds and waters the garden on July 1. Circle the days in July when he needs to water. Put a star next to the days when he needs to weed.

2. On what dates will Jim weed the garden?

   _____

3. On what dates will Jim water the garden?

   _____

4. How many more times will Jim water the garden than weed it?

   _____

Notes for Home: Your child learned how to measure elapsed time in a process. **Home Activity:** Discuss ways your child could have figured out the dates for the calendar. (by counting off days or by adding 3 and 7, respectively, to the date over and over)

Notes

Dear Family,

Your child is learning about different types of plants and their characteristics. In the science chapter Plants and How They Grow, our class has learned about the different parts of plants and the ways each part helps a plant survive. The children have also learned how plants make more plants, and how plants have changed over time.

In addition to learning how different plants live and grow, the children have also learned many new vocabulary words. Help your child to make these words a part of his or her own vocabulary by using them when you talk together about plants.

system
deciduous
pollinate
coniferous
seed leaf
germinate
seedling
fossil
extinct

The following pages include activities that you and your child can do together. By participating in your child's education, you will help to bring the learning home.

Family Science Activity
Take a Nature walk

Materials

- paper and pencil
- markers or crayons
- magnifying lens (optional)
- ruler

Steps

1. Go outside and look for leaves. Your child should collect at least two different types of leaves to bring home.
2. Do not let the leaves dry out. They will be hard to work with when they are brittle.
3. Tell your child to take the leaves and look at them carefully. Draw them in a box on the paper.
4. Use a magnifying lens to look at the veins of the leaves. What else can you see with the magnifying lens?
5. Measure the length and width of each leaf.
6. Take the leaves and trace around them on the paper.
7. Color the leaves traced on the paper to look like the real leaves. Write a few sentences to describe the leaves.

Talk About It

Why do plants have leaves? Do all leaves look alike? What do leaves do for a plant? Do leaves ever change colors? How? When? What happens to a lot of leaves in the fall?

Vocabulary Practice

Unscramble the letters to find the vocabulary words below..

1. NATLELIOP _____

2. NITTEXC _____

3. SERFOUIONC _____

4. TESMSY _____

5. DUDEOUCIS _____

6. IFSOLS _____

7. TREEGMAIN _____

Identifying Parts of Plants

What part of a plant is it? Write if it is a **leaf**, **root**, **stem**, **flower**, or **seed**.

1. Tree trunk _____

2. Pea _____

3. Lettuce _____

4. Corn kernel _____

5. Blade of grass _____

6. Rose _____

7. Carrot _____

Fun Fact

The tallest living plant in the world is a redwood tree in California. This giant tree is over 369 feet tall! Its exact location is kept secret by park rangers to protect the tree.

Choose a word to complete each sentence. Underline clues that helped you decide.

vertebrate	inherited	hibernate	pupa
adaptations	migrate	larva	traits

1. A dog, a fish, and a person are all examples of a _____, or an animal with a backbone.

2. An insect egg may hatch into a _____, which eats a lot and grows fast.

3. _____, such as sharp teeth or webbed feet, help an animal survive where it lives.

4. _____ are body features passed on by an animal to its young.

5. A trait that is always passed on from parents to offspring is said to be _____.

6. A caterpillar forms a hard shell around itself and becomes a _____. When it comes out, it will be an adult.

7. Some animals _____ to the south for the winter. There they can find food.

8. Other animals know when to _____, or slow down their bodies and sleep a long time.

Notes for Home: Your child learned the vocabulary terms for Chapter 2.
Home Activity: Have your child use pictures in the text to provide examples that help define the vocabulary words. Action words can be acted out.

Sequence

Read the paragraph.

Kangaroo

The mother kangaroo gives birth to a tiny baby. It is only about one inch long. As soon as it is born, the baby crawls into its mother's pouch. Once there, it feeds on milk for six to eight months. Finally, it is big enough and strong enough to hop around and eat on its own.

Apply It!

What are the sequence of events in the paragraph about the kangaroo? Fill in the graphic organizer to show the correct order.

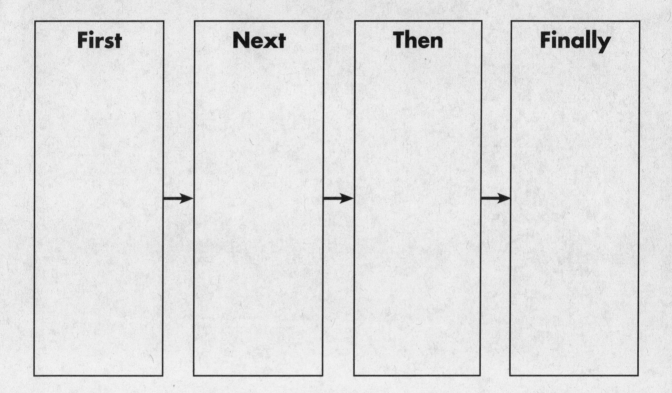

| **First** | **Next** | **Then** | **Finally** |

© Pearson Education, Inc.

Notes for Home: Your child learned how to recognize the sequence of events in a process.

Home Activity: Read a library book with your child about how one animal grows and changes. Talk about the stages in the animal's life, using the words *first, next, then,* and *finally*.

Notes

Lesson 1: How are animals grouped?

Before You Read Lesson 1

Read each statement below. Place a check mark in the circle to indicate whether you agree or disagree with the statement.

	Agree	Disagree
1. There are many more invertebrates than vertebrates.	O	O
2. All vertebrates have a backbone.	O	O
3. Cats are vertebrates, but fish are not.	O	O

After You Read Lesson 1

Reread each statement above. If the lesson supports your choice, place a check mark in the *Correct* circle. Then explain how the text supports your choice. If the lesson does not support your choice, place a check mark in the *Incorrect* circle. Then explain why your choice is wrong.

	Correct	Incorrect
1. _____ _____	O	O
2. _____ _____	O	O
3. _____ _____	O	O

Notes for Home: Your child has completed a pre/post inventory of key concepts in the lesson.
Home Activity: Have your child cut out magazine pictures of animals and group them to show various ways they are similar.

Reviewing Terms: Sentence Completion

Complete the sentence with the correct word or phrase.

_____ 1. _____ are features of animals, like fish's gills or scales. (Traits, Needs)

_____ 2. _____ Cats and dogs are because they have backbones. (vertebrates, invertebrates)

Reviewing Concepts: Matching

Match each vertebrate with the correct group. Write the letter on the line next to each vertebrate.

_____ 3. snake   **a.** mammal

_____ 4. frog   **b.** reptile

_____ 5. dog   **c.** amphibian

Match each invertebrate with the correct group. Write the letter on the line next to each invertebrate.

_____ 6. octopus   **a.** arthropod

_____ 7. crab   **b.** worm

_____ 8. earthworm   **c.** mollusk

Applying Strategies: Calculating

9. On a visit to the zoo, Jennifer's class saw 20 species of fishes, 5 species of amphibians, 10 species of birds, and 12 species of mammals. How many species did they see altogether? Show your work. (2 points)

_____

_____

Name _____

Lesson 2: How do animals grow and change?

Before You Read Lesson 2

Read each statement below. Place a check mark in the circle
to indicate whether you agree or disagree with the statement.

	Agree	Disagree
1. All animals develop inside their mothers.	○	○
2. A butterfly's first stage of life is the pupa.	○	○
3. A very young frog acts much like a fish.	○	○

After You Read Lesson 2

Reread each statement above. If the lesson supports your
choice, place a check mark in the *Correct* circle. Then explain
how the text supports your choice. If the lesson does not
support your choice, place a check mark in the *Incorrect* circle.
Then explain why your choice is wrong.

	Correct	Incorrect
1. _____	○	○
_____		
2. _____	○	○
_____		
3. _____	○	○
_____		

Notes for Home: Your child has completed a pre/post inventory of key concepts in
the lesson.
Home Activity: Have your child compare photographs of himself or herself at
different ages and note how he or she has changed while growing.

Name _____

Lesson 2 Review

Use with pages 44–47.

Reviewing Terms: Matching

Match each definition with the correct word. Write the letter on the line next to each definition.

_____ 1. the first stage of a butterfly's life cycle after hatching from an egg   **a.** larva

_____ 2. the stage of a butterfly's life cycle when it is covered by a hard coating   **b.** pupa

Reviewing Concepts: True or False

Write **T** (True) or **F** (False) on the line before each statement.

_____ 3. All animals have the same steps in their life cycles.

_____ 4. Some animals start their lives as eggs.

_____ 5. Development is the part of an animal's life cycle when it changes into an adult.

_____ 6. An adult butterfly comes out of a larva.

_____ 7. Mammals have more changes in their life cycle than insects or amphibians.

_____ 8. When mammals are born, they drink milk from their mother.

Writing

Use complete sentences to answer question 9. (2 points)

9. Describe one similarity between a butterfly's life cycle and a frog's life cycle. Describe one difference between them.

_____

_____

_____

© Pearson Education, Inc.

17A Lesson Review   Workbook

Lesson 3: How do adaptations help animals?

Before You Read Lesson 3

Read each statement below. Place a check mark in the circle to indicate whether you agree or disagree with the statement.

	Agree	Disagree
1. Body parts are adaptations.	○	○
2. Adaptations must be learned.	○	○
3. When animals migrate, they sleep a long time.	○	○

After You Read Lesson 3

Reread each statement above. If the lesson supports your choice, place a check mark in the *Correct* circle. Then explain how the text supports your choice. If the lesson does not support your choice, place a check mark in the *Incorrect* circle. Then explain why your choice is wrong.

	Correct	Incorrect
1. _____ _____	○	○
2. _____ _____	○	○
3. _____ _____	○	○

Notes for Home: Your child has completed a pre/post inventory of key concepts in the lesson.
Home Activity: Discuss with your child some adaptations a pet (or a wild animal you can observe) has that help it survive.

Reviewing Terms: Matching

Match each definition with the correct word. Write the letter on the line next to each description.

_____ 1. a trait that helps animals meet their needs

_____ 2. when a trait is passed on from parents to their young

_____ 3. when animals move as the seasons change

_____ 4. when an animal's body systems slow down to save energy

a. inherited
b. adaptation
c. migrate
d. hibernate

Reviewing Concepts: True or False

Write **T** (True) or **F** (False) on the line before each statement.

_____ 5. A bird's bill is an adaptation that helps it meet its need for food.

_____ 6. When a harmless animal looks like a poisonous one, it is called camouflage.

_____ 7. An adaptation that allows an animal to blend in with its environment is mimicry.

_____ 8. An instinct is a behavior that an animal is born knowing how to do.

Writing

Use complete sentences to answer question 9. (2 points)

9. Describe two ways that migrating helps animals survive.

_____

_____

Lesson 4: How are animals from the past like today's animals?

Before You Read Lesson 4

Read each statement below. Place a check mark in the circle to indicate whether you agree or disagree with the statement.

	Agree	Disagree
1. A fossil is an animal skeleton.	○	○
2. Fossils show how life on Earth has changed.	○	○
3. Today's desert may have once been a jungle.	○	○

After You Read Lesson 4

Reread each statement above. If the lesson supports your choice, place a check mark in the *Correct* circle. Then explain how the text supports your choice. If the lesson does not support your choice, place a check mark in the *Incorrect* circle. Then explain why your choice is wrong.

	Correct	Incorrect
1. _____ _____	○	○
2. _____ _____	○	○
3. _____ _____	○	○

Notes for Home: Your child has completed a pre/post inventory of key concepts in the lesson.
Home Activity: Have your child use modeling clay to create molds of animal parts, such as a paw or a shell. Talk about how fossils form in nature.

Reviewing Concepts: Sentence Completion

Complete each sentence with the correct word or phrase.

_____ 1. A(n) ____ is a sign of past life. (fossil, extinct)

_____ 2. Only the ____ parts of an animal become a fossil. (hard, soft)

_____ 3. A(n) ____ is formed when rock materials fill a fossil mold. (cast, amber)

_____ 4. Hardened tree sap is called ____. (amber, bone)

_____ 5. The fossils found in tar pits are ____. (actual bone, minerals)

_____ 6. An extinct kind of animal is ____. (no longer living, found everywhere)

_____ 7. Fossils show that Earth has ____ over time. (stayed the same, changed)

_____ 8. Fossils show that ____ animals today resemble extinct animals. (some, all)

Applying Strategies: Sequencing

9. Some insects are preserved in amber. The steps are shown here out of order. Using the clue words in the sentences, write the steps in the correct order. (2 points)

Next, the sap completely covers the insect.
Finally, the sap turns into amber.
First, an insect is trapped in sticky sap.

_____

_____

_____

Name _____

Comparing Animal Traits

A graph helps you compare numbers and amounts. Read the graph. Then answer the questions.

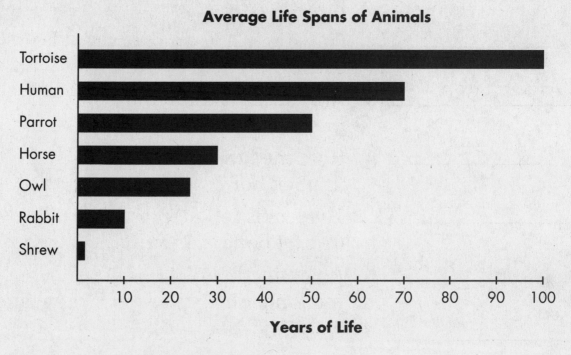

Average Life Spans of Animals

Years of Life

1. How long do most horses live?

    _____

2. Which usually lives longer, a human or a parrot?

    _____

3. Which animal on the graph lives the longest?

    _____

4. A rabbit lives 10 times longer than what animal?

    _____

5. How much longer can you expect to live than a horse?

    _____

 Notes for Home: Your child learned to read a bar graph to compare data about animals.
Home Activity: Make a bar graph comparing the heights of members in your family. Have your child answer questions you ask about the graph.

Notes

Dear Family,

Your child is learning about the lives of different animals. In the science chapter How Animals Live, our class has learned how animals are grouped and about their life cycles. Students have also learned how adaptations help animals live and how fossils tell about animals that lived long ago.

In addition to learning how animals live, grow, and survive, students have also learned many new vocabulary words. Help your child to make these words a part of his or her own vocabulary by using them when you talk together about animals.

trait
vertebrate
larva
pupa
adaptation
inherited
migrate
hibernate

The following pages include activities that you and your child can do together. By participating in your child's education, you will help to bring the learning home.

© Pearson Education, Inc.

Family Science Activity
Play Porcupine

Materials:
- a potato or piece of clay
- markers for coloring
- toothpicks

Steps

1. Use a marker to draw small dots on the surface of the potato or piece of clay. Leave a small area without dots for the head of the porcupine.

2. Take turns pushing toothpicks into the potato or clay. Use the dots you made as a guide. Be careful not to poke yourself. The toothpicks will be the sharp quills of your play porcupine.

3. Use a marker to draw your porcupine's nose, eyes, mouth and ears. You may also look at page 50 of the textbook to see what a porcupine looks like.

4. The porcupine's sharp quills stand up when the porcupine is scared or threatened. The porcupine's quills help protect it. This is called an adaption. Discuss other animals and adaptations they have to protect themselves.

Workbook

Literacy and Art

Animals need shelter. For example, birds build nests for shelter. Draw a picture of an animal. Be sure to draw shelter for the animal. Then, write 2 or 3 details about the animal and where it lives.

Animal Adaptations

Look at the pictures and words below. **Draw** lines to match each animal with the phrase that describes its adaptation.

has sharp quills

sprays a bad smell

has sharp claws

has sharp teeth

looks like a twig

can sting

Workbook

Name _____

Use the words to fill in the map and show how the words are related to each other.

| environment | desert | ecosystem | grassland |
| population | tundra | community | wetland |

All the populations living together in a place form a(n) _____.

The living and nonliving things around each plant and animal form its _____.

Living things in one place and the nonliving things affecting them make a(n) _____.

Every group of one kind of plant or animal in a place is called a(n) _____.

Kinds of Ecosystems

Forests (trees)

_____ (frozen)

_____ (dry, hot)

_____ (prairie)

_____ (swamp)

fresh water (lake, river)

salt water (ocean)

Notes for Home: Your child learned the vocabulary terms for Chapter 3.
Home Activity: Talk with your child about the kinds of ecosystems. Then identify the type of ecosystem that is found nearest your home, or find magazine pictures showing a type of ecosystem.

© Pearson Education, Inc.

Main Idea and Details

Read the science article.

Desert Plants

Plants that live in the dry, hot desert have special adaptations to survive. A cactus, for example, stores water in its thick leaves and stems. Some desert plants have leaves with a waxy covering to hold in water. They grow slowly to save water. They may send roots over a large area of soil to take in water.

Apply It!

In the outer squares, write details that support the main idea in the center circle.

Desert plants are adapted to survive.

© Pearson Education, Inc.

Notes for Home: Your child learned to identify details that support a main idea. **Home Activity:** Read an article about plants or animals with your child. State one main idea of the article. Have your child point out details that support that main idea.

Notes

Name _____

Lesson 1: What are ecosystems?

Before You Read Lesson 1

Read each statement below. Place a check mark in the circle to indicate whether you agree or disagree with the statement.

	Agree	Disagree
1. Environment is the nonliving things around you.	○	○
2. Parts of an ecosystem interact.	○	○
3. A population is all the animals in an area.	○	○

After You Read Lesson 1

Reread each statement above. If the lesson supports your choice, place a check mark in the *Correct* circle. Then explain how the text supports your choice. If the lesson does not support your choice, place a check mark in the *Incorrect* circle. Then explain why your choice is wrong.

	Correct	Incorrect
1. _____ _____	○	○
2. _____ _____	○	○
3. _____ _____	○	○

Notes for Home: Your child has completed a pre/post inventory of key concepts in the lesson.
Home Activity: Talk with your child about the ways your community is different from a community in an ecosystem such as a wetland.

© Pearson Education, Inc.

Reviewing Terms: Matching

Match each description with the correct word. Write the letter on the line next to each description.

_____ 1. everything that surrounds a living thing

_____ 2. the living and nonliving parts that interact in an environment

_____ 3. all of the living things of the same kind that live in the same place at the same time

_____ 4. all of the populations that live in the same place

a. population
b. environment
c. community
d. ecosystem

Reviewing Concepts: True or False

Write **T** (True) or **F** (False) on the line before each statement.

_____ 5. Ecosystems are made up of only living parts.

_____ 6. Living parts of ecosystems depend on one another.

_____ 7. A change in a habitat does not affect the living things in that habitat.

_____ 8. If the plants in an ecosystem die, the animals in the ecosystem will not have enough food.

Applying Concepts: Main Idea and Details

Use complete sentences to answer question 9. (2 points)

9. List three details you would use to support the main idea shown here.

Main Idea: Ecosystems change over time.

Detail: _____

Detail: _____

Detail: _____

© Pearson Education, Inc.

Name _____

Lesson 2: Which ecosystems have few trees?

Before You Read Lesson 2

Read each statement below. Place a check mark in the circle to indicate whether you agree or disagree with the statement.

	Agree	Disagree
1. A grassland is a prairie.	O	O
2. A desert is hot by day and cold by night.	O	O
3. A tundra is too cold for big animals.	O	O

After You Read Lesson 2

Reread each statement above. If the lesson supports your choice, place a check mark in the *Correct* circle. Then explain how the text supports your choice. If the lesson does not support your choice, place a check mark in the *Incorrect* circle. Then explain why your choice is wrong.

	Correct	Incorrect
1. _____ _____	O	O
2. _____ _____	O	O
3. _____ _____	O	O

Notes for Home: Your child has completed a pre/post inventory of key concepts in the lesson.
Home Activity: Identify a land ecosystem found in your area. Together list the plants, animals, and objects that you and your child have seen there.

© Pearson Education, Inc.

Workbook

Reviewing Terms: Matching

Match each description with the correct word. Write the letter on the line next to each description.

_____ 1. a land ecosystem with grasses and flowering plants

_____ 2. a land ecosystem that gets very little rain

_____ 3. a cold, dry land ecosystem

a. tundra
b. desert
c. grassland

Reviewing Concepts: Sentence Completion

Complete each sentence with the correct word.

_____ 4. Grasses survive in grasslands because they have _____ roots. (deep, shallow).

_____ 5. Cactuses are plants found in _____. (deserts, grasslands)

_____ 6. Desert plants can live with very little _____. (sunlight, rainfall)

_____ 7. Winters in the _____ are long and cold. (desert, tundra)

_____ 8. In the tundra, soil below the surface stays _____ all year. (wet, frozen)

Applying Strategies: Compare and Contrast

Use complete sentences to answer question 9. (2 points)

9. Name one way in which deserts, tundra, and grasslands are all alike and one way in which they are different.

_____

_____

_____

_____

© Pearson Education, Inc.

Lesson 3: What are some forest ecosystems?

Before You Read Lesson 3

Read each statement below. Place a check mark in the circle to indicate whether you agree or disagree with the statement.

	Agree	Disagree
1. Tropical forests lie near the equator.	O	O
2. Trees in deciduous forests drop their leaves in fall.	O	O
3. Coniferous forests get the most rain.	O	O

After You Read Lesson 3

Reread each statement above. If the lesson supports your choice, place a check mark in the *Correct* circle. Then explain how the text supports your choice. If the lesson does not support your choice, place a check mark in the *Incorrect* circle. Then explain why your choice is wrong.

	Correct	Incorrect
1. _____ _____	O	O
2. _____ _____	O	O
3. _____ _____	O	O

Notes for Home: Your child has completed a pre/post inventory of key concepts in the lesson.
Home Activity: With your child, observe some evergreen needles and some broadleaf leaves. Ask your child to tell how they are different.

Reviewing Concepts: Matching

Match each description with the correct kind of forest. Write the letter on the line next to each description. You can use each answer more than once.

_____ 1. These grow mainly in northern North America, Europe, and Asia.

_____ 2. Oak, maple, and beech trees are found in these.

_____ 3. These have a climate that is warm and rainy all year long.

_____ 4. Spruce, fir, and pine trees are found in these.

_____ 5. Trees with leaves that look like needles are found in these.

_____ 6. Mosses and lichens are some of the things that can live on the floor of these.

_____ 7. These grow near the equator.

_____ 8. Sunlight reaches the forest floor during a part of the year in these.

a. coniferous forests

b. deciduous forests

c. tropical forests

Applying Strategies: Converting Units

9. A tropical rainforest gets an average of 300 centimeters of rain each year. How many meters of rain is this? There are 100 centimeters in 1 meter. Show your work. (2 points)

_____

_____

_____

Lesson 4: What are water ecosystems?

Before You Read Lesson 4

Read each statement below. Place a check mark in the circle to indicate whether you agree or disagree with the statement.

	Agree	Disagree
1. A wetland is a freshwater ecosystem.	○	○
2. Most life in the oceans is at the bottom.	○	○
3. Saltwater ecosystems cover most of the world.	○	○

After You Read Lesson 4

Reread each statement above. If the lesson supports your choice, place a check mark in the *Correct* circle. Then explain how the text supports your choice. If the lesson does not support your choice, place a check mark in the *Incorrect* circle. Then explain why your choice is wrong.

	Correct	Incorrect
1. _____ _____	○	○
2. _____ _____	○	○
3. _____ _____	○	○

Notes for Home: Your child has completed a pre/post inventory of key concepts in the lesson.
Home Activity: With your child, observe an aquarium (or read about setting one up). Together list the things needed for this freshwater ecosystem.

Reviewing Terms: Sentence Completion

Complete each sentence with the correct word or phrase.

_____ 1. A low land covered by water at least part of the year is a _____. (wetland, tropical forest)

Reviewing Concepts: True or False

Write **T** (True) or **F** (False) on the line before each statement.

_____ 2. Lakes, ponds, and rivers are usually saltwater ecosystems.

_____ 3. Rivers and streams are moving water.

_____ 4. Water flows very quickly through the Everglades in Florida.

_____ 5. Animals do not live in the Everglades.

_____ 6. Ocean water is salt water.

_____ 7. Most living things in the ocean live at the very bottom.

_____ 8. Salt marshes form where river water mixes with ocean water.

Writing

Use complete sentences to answer question 9. (2 points)

9. Describe two ways that wetlands are important to animals.

_____

_____

_____

_____

Comparing Data

Look at the graph. Use it to answer the questions.

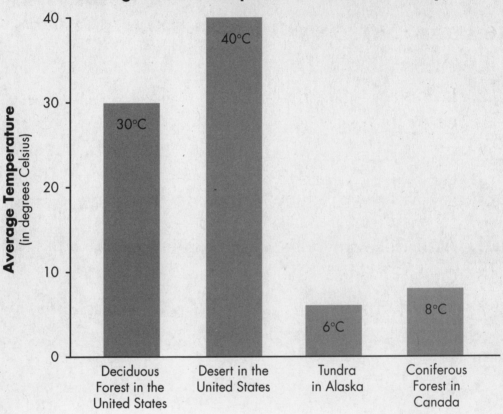

Average Summer Temperatures in Different Ecosystems

Questions

1. Which ecosystem is hottest?

   _____

2. Which ecosystem is coldest?

   _____

3. Which ecosystems have very close temperatures?

   _____

Notes for Home: Your child learned how to read and use a graph.
Home Activity: Find a graph in a newspaper or magazine. Review the data with your child and ask questions about the data.

Notes

Dear Family,

Your child is learning about different environments where plants and animals live together. In the science chapter Where Plants and Animals Live, our class has learned about land ecosystems, including some with few trees and others with forests. The children have also learned about water ecosystems, such as rivers, salt marshes, and oceans.

In addition to learning where plants and animals live, the children have also learned many new vocabulary words. Help your child to make these words a part of his or her own vocabulary by using them when you talk together about different ecosystems.

> environment
> ecosystem
> population
> community
> grassland
> desert
> tundra
> wetland

The following pages include activities that you and your child can do together. By participating in your child's education, you will help to bring the learning home.

Family Science Activity
At Home in a Forest Ecosystem

Materials:
- colored pencils and markers
- white drawing paper

Steps:

1. Talk with your child about forests. Have you been to a forest? What kinds of plants and animals did you see? Have you seen any of these plants and animals?

    Plants: oak trees, evergreen trees, shrubs
    Animals: woodpeckers, rabbits, foxes, beavers, deer, bears

2. Read the following list of plants and animals.

3. Dicuss the forest ecosystem. The forest has large plants such as oak trees that create shade for small plants. The plants provide habitat for small animals. Large animals such as foxes and bears survive by eating plants and smaller animals.

4. Have your child draw a scene of a forest on a sheet of drawing paper. They may copy or trace pictures from page 2 of this booklet. Your child can also draw nonliving things that are part of the forest ecosystem, such as rocks, soil and water.

5. Ask your child to label each plant and animal in the drawing. Encourage your child to explain the drawing and display the picture for others to see.

Workbook

Look at the pictures and words below.
Draw lines to match the pictures and words.

oak tree

evergreen tree

shrub

rabbit

fox

bear

What Is There?

Write the name of one living thing and one nonliving thing that you can find in each one of these ecosystems.

Grassland _____ _____

Desert _____ _____

Tundra _____ _____

Forest _____ _____

Wetland _____ _____

Ocean _____ _____

Name _____

Think about each word or set of words. Write the words to complete the outline.

I. germs

   A. What do they do? Germs cause _____.

   B. Examples of germs: _____

II. producer, consumer, predator, prey

   A. How do they get food? _____ make their own food. _____ eat food.

   B. Who eats whom? A _____ eats other animals, which are called _____.

III. herbivore, carnivore, omnivore

   A. How are they alike? They are all types of _____.

   B. How are they different? _____ eat only plants. _____ eat only animals. _____ eat both plants and animals.

IV. competition

   A. What is it? _____

   _____

   B. When does it happen? _____

   _____

Notes for Home: Your child learned the vocabulary terms for Chapter 4.
Home Activity: Have your child cut out magazine pictures or draw pictures to illustrate each vocabulary term.

Draw Conclusions

Read the paragraph.

Jose Becomes Ill

Jose is beginning to get a fever and a sore throat. Last week, his little sister had a cold. They usually play with the same toys at home.

Apply It!

Write facts from the paragraph in the small boxes on the next page. Then write your conclusion in the big box.

Fact

_____

_____

Fact

_____

_____

Fact

_____

_____

Conclusion

_____

_____

_____

_____

_____

_____

_____

Notes for Home: Your child learned to draw conclusions from facts.
Home Activity: Give your child sets of facts about animals. Help him or her draw logical conclusions based on the facts.

Notes

Lesson 1: How do living things interact?

Before You Read Lesson 1

Read each statement below. Place a check mark in the circle to indicate whether you agree or disagree with the statement.

	Agree	Disagree
1. Animals may live in groups to protect each other.	○	○
2. A bee visits a flower, and both benefit.	○	○
3. Different kinds of living things do not help each other.	○	○

After You Read Lesson 1

Reread each statement above. If the lesson supports your choice, place a check mark in the *Correct* circle. Then explain how the text supports your choice. If the lesson does not support your choice, place a check mark in the *Incorrect* circle. Then explain why your choice is wrong.

	Correct	Incorrect
1. _____ _____	○	○
2. _____ _____	○	○
3. _____ _____	○	○

Notes for Home: Your child has completed a pre/post inventory of key concepts in the lesson.
Home Activity: Together observe an animal interaction, such as a pet getting food from you. Talk about how the interaction helps the animal(s) survive.

Reviewing Concepts: Matching

Match the examples with the correct description of the way living things interact. Write the letter on the line next to each description. You can use each answer more than once.

_____ 1. members of a herd protecting each other

_____ 2. a cleaner fish getting food when it cleans a larger fish

_____ 3. a bee "dancing" to show other bees where flowers are

_____ 4. a tree helping a flower get light, the flower does not help or harm the tree

_____ 5. a prairie dog whistling to warn its group of predators

_____ 6. a bee getting food when it pollinates a flower

_____ 7. barnacles living on whales, the whales are not helped or harmed

_____ 8. a moth pollinating a yucca plant and laying its eggs in the plant

a. helping in groups

b. one kind helping another

c. two kinds helping each other

Applying Concepts: Draw Conclusions

Use complete sentences to answer question 9. (2 points)

9. Read the three facts below. Then write a conclusion that is supported by the facts.

Fact 1: Sometimes animals help others in their group.

Fact 2: Sometimes one kind of animal helps another kind.

Fact 3: Sometimes two kinds of animals help each other.

Conclusion: _____

_____

Lesson 2: How do living things get energy?

Before You Read Lesson 2

Read each statement below. Place a check mark in the circle to indicate whether you agree or disagree with the statement.

	Agree	Disagree
1. All animals are consumers.	○	○
2. Producers get their energy from food.	○	○
3. Many food chains make a food web.	○	○

After You Read Lesson 2

Reread each statement above. If the lesson supports your choice, place a check mark in the *Correct* circle. Then explain how the text supports your choice. If the lesson does not support your choice, place a check mark in the *Incorrect* circle. Then explain why your choice is wrong.

	Correct	Incorrect
1. _____ _____	○	○
2. _____ _____	○	○
3. _____ _____	○	○

Notes for Home: Your child has completed a pre/post inventory of key concepts in the lesson.
Home Activity: List some foods your family has eaten today. Have your child classify them as plant or animal. Talk about where each got its energy from.

Reviewing Terms: Matching

Match each description with the correct word. Write the letter on the line next to each description.

_____ 1. a living thing that makes food
_____ 2. a living thing that eats food
_____ 3. a consumer that eats only plants
_____ 4. a consumer that eats only animals
_____ 5. a consumer that eats both plants and animals
_____ 6. any animal that is hunted by others for food
_____ 7. a consumer that hunts for food

a. prey
b. consumer
c. omnivore
d. predator
e. producer
f. herbivore
g. carnivore

Reviewing Concepts: Sentence Completion

Complete the sentence with the correct word.

_____ 8. Food chains and food webs show how _____ moves between living things. (water, energy)

Applying Strategies: Calculating

9. In one food chain, ferrets eat prairie dogs. If each ferret eats 4 prairie dogs each month, how many prairie dogs would be eaten by 11 ferrets in one month? Show your work. (2 points)

Lesson 3: How do living things compete?

Before You Read Lesson 3

Read each statement below. Place a check mark in the circle to indicate whether you agree or disagree with the statement.

	Agree	Disagree
1. Animals compete, but plants do not.	○	○
2. Two predators might compete for prey.	○	○
3. Living things compete for food, water, and space.	○	○

After You Read Lesson 3

Reread each statement above. If the lesson supports your choice, place a check mark in the *Correct* circle. Then explain how the text supports your choice. If the lesson does not support your choice, place a check mark in the *Incorrect* circle. Then explain why your choice is wrong.

	Correct	Incorrect
1. _____ _____	○	○
2. _____ _____	○	○
3. _____ _____	○	○

Notes for Home: Your child has completed a pre/post inventory of key concepts in the lesson.
Home Activity: Observe some plants near your home. Discuss with your child how they are competing for the same space, food, and water and predict which will win.

Reviewing Terms: Sentence Completion

Complete each sentence with the correct word.

_____ 1. When two or more living things need the same resources, they are in _____ with one another. (cooperation, competition)

Reviewing Concepts: True or False

Write **T** (True) or **F** (False) on the line before each statement.

_____ 2. Living things compete for many kinds of resources.

_____ 3. Animals do not compete for mates.

_____ 4. Animals that are good predators pass those traits to their young.

_____ 5. Prey often compete to get predators.

_____ 6. Sometimes people and animals compete for space.

_____ 7. Some living things compete for oxygen.

_____ 8. Competition between animals sometimes follows cycles.

Writing

Use complete sentences to answer question 9. (2 points)

9. Write a short paragraph that describes two kinds of birds competing for a resource they both need to survive.

_____

_____

_____

_____

_____

Name _____

Lesson 4: How do environments change?

Before You Read Lesson 4

Read each statement below. Place a check mark in the circle to indicate whether you agree or disagree with the statement.

	Agree	Disagree
1. Living things can change their environment.	○	○
2. Fire destroys a forest forever.	○	○
3. Environment changes often occur in patterns.	○	○

After You Read Lesson 4

Reread each statement above. If the lesson supports your choice, place a check mark in the *Correct* circle. Then explain how the text supports your choice. If the lesson does not support your choice, place a check mark in the *Incorrect* circle. Then explain why your choice is wrong.

	Correct	Incorrect
1. _____ _____	○	○
2. _____ _____	○	○
3. _____ _____	○	○

Notes for Home: Your child has completed a pre/post inventory of key concepts in the lesson.
Home Activity: Point out a community environment that has changed, such as a construction site. Ask your child how this change affected the organisms that live there.

© Pearson Education, Inc.

Reviewing Terms: Sentence Completion

Complete each sentence with the correct word.

_____ 1. A living thing that breaks down waste and living things that have died is a _____. (decomposer, decay)

_____ 2. _____ is the process of breaking down waste and living things that have died. (Decomposer, Decay)

Reviewing Concepts: Matching

Living things and natural events can cause environments to change. For each description of change listed below, show whether it is a change caused by a living thing or a natural event. You can use each answer more than once.

_____ 3. A volcano erupts and kills plants in an environment.

a. a living thing

_____ 4. A hurricane knocks down trees.

b. a natural event

_____ 5. A forest fire burns plants and trees.

_____ 6. A person chops down trees to make space to build a house.

_____ 7. A drought causes many plants to die.

_____ 8. A beaver's dam floods an area.

Applying Strategies: Cause and Effect

Use complete sentences to answer question 9. (2 points)

9. Write three causes of environmental change.

Cause: _____

Cause: _____

Cause: _____

Effect: An environment is changed.

Lesson 5: What is a healthy environment for people?

Before You Read Lesson 5

Read each statement below. Place a check mark in the circle to indicate whether you agree or disagree with the statement.

	Agree	Disagree
1. Food and water are all people need to live.	◯	◯
2. To get needed nutrients, we should eat a variety of foods.	◯	◯
3. Dairy products help grow strong bones.	◯	◯

After You Read Lesson 5

Reread each statement above. If the lesson supports your choice, place a check mark in the *Correct* circle. Then explain how the text supports your choice. If the lesson does not support your choice, place a check mark in the *Incorrect* circle. Then explain why your choice is wrong.

	Correct	Incorrect
1. _____ _____	◯	◯
2. _____ _____	◯	◯
3. _____ _____	◯	◯

Notes for Home: Your child has completed a pre/post inventory of key concepts in the lesson.
Home Activity: Plan a healthful lunch with your child. Together prepare the meal. Enjoy your lunch as you discuss the importance of eating a variety of foods.

Reviewing Concepts: True or False

Write **T** (True) or **F** (False) on the line before each statement.

_____ 1. People need food to survive.

_____ 2. Not all people need water.

_____ 3. People need to live in a clean environment.

_____ 4. Shelter helps people stay at a comfortable temperature.

_____ 5. Only people in cities need air to live.

_____ 6. Eating a variety of foods helps people stay healthy.

_____ 7. People who handle food should have clean hands.

_____ 8. The digestive system takes in the air people need to live.

Applying Strategies: Sequencing

Use complete sentences to answer question 9. (2 points)

9. The steps of what happens to food in the digestive system are shown out of order. Using the clue words in the sentences, write the steps in the correct order.

Next, food is mixed with digestive juices in the stomach.
Finally, solid waste is formed in the large intestine.
First, the teeth break food into pieces.
Then food particles pass into the bloodstream through the small intestine walls.

_____

_____

_____

_____

_____

© Pearson Education, Inc.

Lesson 6: How can people stay healthy?

Before You Read Lesson 6

Read each statement below. Place a check mark in the circle to indicate whether you agree or disagree with the statement.

	Agree	Disagree
1. Exercise helps the heart, lungs, and muscles.	◯	◯
2. Your lungs are part of your circulatory system.	◯	◯
3. Bacteria and viruses are germs.	◯	◯

After You Read Lesson 6

Reread each statement above. If the lesson supports your choice, place a check mark in the *Correct* circle. Then explain how the text supports your choice. If the lesson does not support your choice, place a check mark in the *Incorrect* circle. Then explain why your choice is wrong.

	Correct	Incorrect
1. _____ _____	◯	◯
2. _____ _____	◯	◯
3. _____ _____	◯	◯

Notes for Home: Your child has completed a pre/post inventory of key concepts in the lesson.
Home Activity: Talk with your child about a time he or she became ill. Discuss how it happened and what you did to help your child get better.

Reviewing Terms: Matching

Match each description with the correct word or phrase. Write the letter on the line next to each description.

_____ 1. very small living things or particles that can cause disease

_____ 2. conditions in which parts of the body do not work properly

a. diseases
b. germs

Reviewing Concepts: Sentence Completion

Complete each sentence with the correct word.

_____ 3. Sports and yard work are good ways to get _____. (exercise, rest)

_____ 4. Lungs are a part of the _____ system. (respiratory, circulatory)

_____ 5. The heart is a part of the _____ system. (digestive, circulatory)

_____ 6. The windpipe is a tube that leads to the _____. (heart, lungs)

_____ 7. Flu and chicken pox are caused by _____. (germs, exercise)

_____ 8. Exercise and rest can help people stay _____. (sick, healthy)

Applying Strategies: Converting

9. For one week, Tara's family recorded the number of hours and minutes they exercised. By the end of the week, Tara had exercised for 2 hours and 25 minutes. Show the amount of time that Tara exercised in minutes. Remember, 60 minutes are equal to 1 hour. Show your work. (2 points)

© Pearson Education, Inc.

Health by the Numbers

Read the cereal labels. Then answer the questions.

Tasty Squares	**Oaty Bits**
Serving Size: 1 cup	Serving Size: 1 cup
Calories: 170	Calories: 150
Total Fat: 2.0 grams	Total Fat: 1.0 grams
Cholesterol: 0 grams	Cholesterol: 0 grams
Sodium: 180 milligrams	Sodium: 95 milligrams
Carbohydrates: 39 grams	Carbohydrates: 25 grams
Fiber: 3 grams	Fiber: 10 grams
Sugar: 15 grams	Sugar: 11 grams

1. Jeb had two servings of Tasty Squares. How many calories did he eat? _____

2. Pauline had three servings of Oaty Bits. How much sodium did she eat? _____

3. How many more grams of carbohydrates are in a serving of Tasty Squares than in a serving of Oaty Bits?

   _____

4. You should get 25 grams of fiber a day. How many servings of each cereal would it take to get 25 grams of fiber?

   Tasty Squares _____

   Oaty Bits _____

Notes for Home: Your child learned to read labels, compare their data, and solve problems based on the data.
Home Activity: Together compare the labels of several cereals your child eats. Rank them according to the amount of sugar, and then the amount of fiber.

Notes

Dear Family,

Your child is learning about different ways that plants and animals interact. In the science chapter Plants and Animals Living Together, our class learned how food energy moves from one living thing to another. We read how plants, animals, and natural events can change environments. Students also learned what people need in order to be healthy and to stay healthy.

In addition to learning how plants and animals interact with their environment, students also learned many new vocabulary words. Help your child to make these words a part of his or her own vocabulary by using them when you talk together about plants and animals living together.

producer	consumer	herbivore
carnivore	omnivore	predator
prey	competition	decomposer
decay	disease	germs

The following pages include activities that you and your child can do together. By participating in your child's education, you will help to bring the learning home.

Family Science Activity
Observing Decomposers at Work

Materials:

- water
- piece of leftover bread or cheese
- piece of leftover fruit or vegetable
- clear glass jar with a lid
- tape

Steps

1. Wet each piece of food and put it into the jar. Make sure that the pieces are not touching. Put the lid on the container. Seal the edge of the lid with tape.

2. Ask your child to predict which decomposers will help break down the food.

3. Draw a chart with two columns. Label each column with one of the foods you put in the jar. Draw seven rows and label them Day 1 through Day 7.

4. Observe the food once a day for a week. As mold grows on the food, ask your child to write down what the mold looks like, where it grows, and what it does.

5. At the end of the week, discuss what you observed with your child. What decomposers did you see? Where did they grow? Did the same kinds of mold grow on both pieces of food? Did they look the same or different?

Workbook

Vocabulary Practice

Find 9 vocabulary words in the puzzle below and circle them.

```
R  C  A  R  N  I  V  O  R  E  C
P  R  E  D  A  T  O  R  X  P  O
C  O  M  P  E  T  I  T  I  O  N
U  M  R  Q  O  M  A  J  V  S  U
D  N  E  B  R  G  C  G  U
O  I  K  Y  A  C  E  D  L  U  M
R  V  S  I  Z  R  R  K  O  M  E
P  O  Q  B  A  M  C  J  F  R
W  R  E  L  D  I  S  E  A  S  E
H  E  R  B  I  V  O  R  E  P  R
```

Kinds of Consumers

What kind of consumer is it? Write if each animal is an herbivore, a carnivore, or an omnivore.

Cow:
eats plants

_____

Shark:
eats meat

_____

Rabbit:
eats plants

_____

Person:
eats meat and plants

_____

Wolf:
eats meat

_____

Use the vocabulary words in the box to complete the labels on the diagram.

condensation
wetlands
evaporation
water vapor
precipitation
water cycle
groundwater

Water on Earth moves through

a _____.

The Sun can turn water into a gas through

_____.

_____

happens when the gas cools to form water drops.

This gas, called

_____,

is in the air.

These drops of water may fall from clouds as

_____.

Water is found in oceans, lakes,

rivers, and _____

on Earth's surface.

Some water is stored inside the Earth as

_____.

Notes for Home: Your child learned the vocabulary terms for Chapter 5.
Home Activity: Use vocabulary words as you talk with your child about how water changes form. Show evaporation and condensation using boiling water and a glass of ice water.

Cause and Effect

Read the science article.

What Happens to Rain?

What happens to the rain that falls? Some of it sinks into the ground. Some of it runs off into rivers and streams. And some of it rests in puddles. Over time, warmth from the Sun strikes water in puddles, causing it to evaporate. This water then becomes water vapor in the air.

Water vapor rises in the atmosphere. The higher it goes, the cooler the air becomes. When the water vapor becomes cool enough, it condenses. This means it forms droplets of water.

Name _____

Apply It!

Write the cause or causes for each effect in the boxes.

Cause(s)

Effect(s)

1. Puddles evaporate.
2. Water vapor goes into air.

Water droplets form.

Notes for Home: Your child learned how to identify causes and effects.
Home Activity: Together read a newspaper or science magazine article that explains a process. Talk with your child about causes and effects the process explains.

© Pearson Education, Inc.

Notes

Lesson 1: Why is water important?

Before You Read Lesson 1

Read each statement below. Place a check mark in the circle to indicate whether you agree or disagree with the statement.

	Agree	Disagree
1. Your body is about two-thirds water.	○	○
2. People use moving water to make electricity.	○	○
3. Earth's surface is covered with groundwater.	○	○

After You Read Lesson 1

Reread each statement above. If the lesson supports your choice, place a check mark in the *Correct* circle. Then explain how the text supports your choice. If the lesson does not support your choice, place a check mark in the *Incorrect* circle. Then explain why your choice is wrong.

	Correct	Incorrect
1. _____ _____	○	○
2. _____ _____	○	○
3. _____ _____	○	○

 Notes for Home: Your child has completed a pre/post inventory of key concepts in the lesson.
Home Activity: Help your child chart how much water he or she drinks in a day. Encourage him or her to drink eight glasses a day.

Reviewing Terms: Sentence Completion

Complete each sentence with the correct word or phrase.

_____ 1. Water that is an invisible gas found in the air is called _____. (water vapor, groundwater)

_____ 2. A _____ is a place with wet or water-covered ground. (groundwater, wetland)

_____ 3. Water that collects in spaces between underground rocks is called _____. (groundwater, ocean water)

Reviewing Concepts: True or False

Write **T** (True) or **F** (False) on the line before each statement.

_____ 4. Plants need water to make their own food.

_____ 5. Most animals can live without water.

_____ 6. The power of moving water can be used to make electricity.

_____ 7. Ocean water is used for drinking and washing clothes.

_____ 8. Many animals live in wetlands.

Writing

Use complete sentences to answer question 9. (2 points)

9. Describe one way that fresh water and ocean water are alike. Then describe one way they are different.

_____

_____

_____

Lesson 2: How do forms of water change?

Before You Read Lesson 2

Read each statement below. Place a check mark in the circle to indicate whether you agree or disagree with the statement.

	Agree	Disagree
1. The water cycle gives us a supply of fresh water.	○	○
2. At 32 degrees Fahrenheit, water becomes a gas.	○	○
3. Water becomes a gas by evaporation.	○	○

After You Read Lesson 2

Reread each statement above. If the lesson supports your choice, place a check mark in the *Correct* circle. Then explain how the text supports your choice. If the lesson does not support your choice, place a check mark in the *Incorrect* circle. Then explain why your choice is wrong.

	Correct	Incorrect
1. _____ _____	○	○
2. _____ _____	○	○
3. _____ _____	○	○

Notes for Home: Your child has completed a pre/post inventory of key concepts in the lesson.
Home Activity: Talk about a rainstorm you and your child have experienced. Discuss how the rain formed and how water evaporated from puddles.

Reviewing Terms: Matching

Match each definition with the correct word or phrase. Write the letter on the line next to each definition.

_____ 1. movement of water back and forth between air and the Earth's surface

_____ 2. rain, snow, and sleet

_____ 3. water vapor changing to a liquid

_____ 4. liquid water becoming a gas

a. condensation
b. water cycle
c. evaporation
d. precipitation

Reviewing Concepts: Sentence Completion

Complete each sentence with the correct word.

_____ 5. _____ is the process that causes dew to form. (Evaporation, Condensation)

_____ 6. The Sun's energy and _____ cause evaporation as water moves through the water cycle. (wind, sleet)

_____ 7. The form of precipitation depends on the _____ at the Earth's surface. (condensation, temperature)

_____ 8. Dirt, germs, and _____ are removed from water at a water-treatment plant. (fluoride, salt)

Applying Strategies: Identifying Cause and Effect

Use complete sentences to answer question 9. (2 points)

9. If the water in a lake is liquid, identify what must happen to the temperature to cause the water to become ice.

_____

_____

Symmetry and Shapes

Some shapes have symmetry. They are exactly the same on both sides of a line of symmetry. A symmetrical shape may have one, two, or more lines of symmetry.

Look at the figures. Use them to answer the questions.

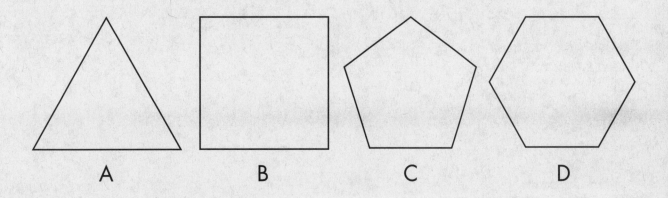

A   B   C   D

1. Which of these figures are symmetrical? _____

2. Which figure has only five lines of symmetry? _____

3. How many lines of symmetry does the square have? Trace the square and show these lines. _____

_____

_____

Notes for Home: Your child learned how to identify symmetry in geometric figures and to draw lines of symmetry.
Home Activity: Use cookie-cutter shapes to cut out dough or clay. Help your child identify which shapes have symmetry and which do not.

Notes

Dear Family,

Your child is learning about the ways in which water is important to life on Earth. In the science chapter Water, our class has learned how water changes phases and how it moves around Earth. The children have also learned different ways that people clean water.

In addition to learning about the uses of water, the children have also learned many new vocabulary words. Help your child to make these words a part of his or her own vocabulary by using them when you talk together about water.

water vapor
groundwater
wetlands
evaporation
condensation
water cycle
precipitation

The following pages include activities that you and your child can do together. By participating in your child's education, you will help to bring the learning home.

Family Science Activity
Evaporation Experiments

Materials:

- four identical, disposable plastic cups
- a grease pencil or permanent marker
- plastic wrap
- a rubber band

Steps

1. Talk about evaporation with your child. Evaporation is when water in liquid form goes into the air and becomes a gas called water vapor. Ask your child to predict how heat will affect the evaporation of water.

2. Help your child pour the same amount of water into each plastic cup.

3. Draw a line on each cup with the grease pencil or marker to mark the water level.

4. Cover two of the cups with plastic wrap and put a rubber band around each cup to seal the plastic cover.

5. Put one uncovered cup and one covered cup in a warm place. Put the other two cups in a cool place. Choose places where the water will not be disturbed.

6. Check each cup every day for a week with your child. When the water level in a cup changes, mark the new water level on the cup with the grease pencil or marker.

7. At the end of the week, compare the water levels in the four cups. Talk with your child about how much water evaporated from each cup. How did heat affect the evaporation of water in the uncovered cups? What happened to the water in the covered cups?

Literacy and Art

Look at the picture and words below.
Draw lines to match the pictures and the words.

Rain

Water Faucet

River

Snowflake (snow)

Ice

Draw It!

Make a drawing that shows different places we can find water and the different forms it can take.

Use the vocabulary words in the box to complete the labels on the diagram. Use your own words to add more examples.

weather	hurricane	tornado	blizzard

includes: air temperature, water in air, wind, and clouds

has patterns: cold, snowy winters

_____

_____

_____

_____ is all around us.

has storms:

A _____ is a huge storm over the ocean.

A _____ is a spinning column of air that touches the ground.

A _____ is a winter storm with great cold and blowing snow.

Notes for Home: Your child learned the vocabulary terms for Chapter 6.
Home Activity: Talk with your child about today's weather. Take turns making statements about the temperature, wind, clouds, and amount of moisture in the air.

TARGET SKILL Make Inferences

Read the paragraph.

Hurricane Warning

The weather forecasters put out a hurricane warning for the Gulf Coast of Florida. The hurricane would hit land in two days. People were busy nailing wood over their windows. They bought extra food and water. Some people got in their cars and drove inland.

Apply It!

What inference can you make from the facts in the paragraph? Write the facts and your inference in the graphic organizer on page 55.

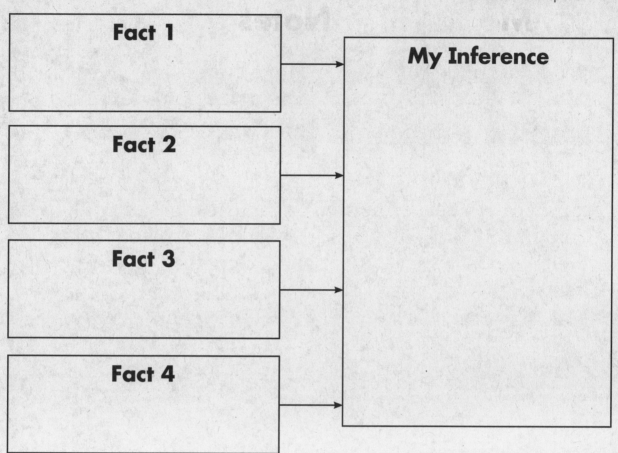

Fact 1

Fact 2

Fact 3

Fact 4

My Inference

Notes for Home: Your child learned how to evaluate the facts to make an inference.
Home Activity: Describe a situation, for example: "You wake to find the grass wet and puddles on the street." Have your child make an inference about what happened.

Notes

Name _____

Lesson 1: What makes up weather?

Before You Read Lesson 1

Read each statement below. Place a check mark in the circle to indicate whether you agree or disagree with the statement.

	Agree	Disagree
1. Atmosphere is the blanket of gases around the Earth.	○	○
2. A barometer measures wind speed.	○	○
3. Air pressure is low when the air presses down a lot.	○	○

After You Read Lesson 1

Reread each statement above. If the lesson supports your choice, place a check mark in the *Correct* circle. Then explain how the text supports your choice. If the lesson does not support your choice, place a check mark in the *Incorrect* circle. Then explain why your choice is wrong.

	Correct	Incorrect
1. _____ _____	○	○
2. _____	○	○
3. _____ _____	○	○

 Notes for Home: Your child has completed a pre-/post-inventory of key concepts in the lesson.
Home Activity: Together watch or read a weather forecast. Talk with your child about a weather pattern that has occurred this week, such as a thunderstorm followed by clear, dry air.

Reviewing Terms: Sentence Completion

Complete each sentence with the correct word.

_____ 1. The blanket of air that surrounds Earth is the _____. (anemometer, atmosphere)

_____ 2. _____ is the temperature, clouds, precipitation, and wind conditions in an area. (Weather, Pollution)

Reviewing Concepts: True or False

Write **T** (True) or **F** (False) on the line before each statement.

_____ 3. Clouds are made up of water droplets in the air.

_____ 4. There is one kind of cloud.

_____ 5. Earth's atmosphere has layers that have different temperatures than one another.

_____ 6. The force of the atmosphere pressing down is called air pressure.

_____ 7. Humidity is the amount of water vapor in the air.

_____ 8. Weather data can be gathered with satellites.

Applying Strategies: Making Inferences

Use complete sentences to answer question 9. (2 points)

9. Terry checked the barometer reading several times during the day. The barometer reading was lower each time she checked. What does a barometer measure? What weather conditions could Terry expect?

_____

_____

_____

Name _____

Lesson 2: How does weather affect people?

Before You Read Lesson 2

Read each statement below. Place a check mark in the circle to indicate whether you agree or disagree with the statement.

	Agree	Disagree
1. In most places, the weather changes in a pattern.	○	○
2. A blizzard is a dangerous winter storm.	○	○
3. A hurricane is a spinning cloud on the ground.	○	○

After You Read Lesson 2

Reread each statement above. If the lesson supports your choice, place a check mark in the *Correct* circle. Then explain how the text supports your choice. If the lesson does not support your choice, place a check mark in the *Incorrect* circle. Then explain why your choice is wrong.

	Correct	Incorrect
1. _____ _____	○	○
2. _____ _____	○	○
3. _____ _____	○	○

Notes for Home: Your child has completed a pre-/post-inventory of key concepts in the lesson.
Home Activity: Talk with your child about a storm that can occur in your area (thunderstorm, hurricane, tornado, blizzard). List safety tips and ways to prepare for the storm.

© Pearson Education, Inc.

Reviewing Terms: Matching

Match each definition with the correct word. Write the letter on the line next to each definition.

_____ 1. a winter storm with blowing snow

_____ 2. a storm with a funnel-shaped column of air that touches the ground

_____ 3. storms with heavy rain, strong winds, and huge waves

a. hurricane
b. blizzard
c. tornado

Reviewing Concepts: Sentence Completion

Complete the sentence with the correct word or phrase.

_____ 4. Patterns of weather are _____ everywhere on Earth. (different, the same)

_____ 5. As air moves up a mountain it gets _____. (colder, wetter)

_____ 6. All deserts are _____. (hot, dry)

_____ 7. Heavy rains and very high waves can both cause _____. (floods, blizzards)

_____ 8. Hurricanes, tornados, and blizzards all have _____. (wind, low temperatures)

Writing

Use a complete sentence to answer question 9. (2 points)

9. Write a sentence that describes one way the National Weather Service helps to keep people safe.

_____

_____

_____

Comparing Temperatures

The table shows temperatures for the town of Smithport. Each temperature represents the average daytime high for July in a certain year. Do you see a pattern?

Changes in High Temperature for Smithport, 1980–2005

Year	1980	1985	1990	1995	2000	2005
Average daytime high for July	79°	79°	81°	80°	83°	84°

Use the table to answer these questions.

1. What trend, or pattern, do you see happening over 25 years?

   _____

2. When did the biggest change occur?

   _____

3. How much warmer was it, on average, in July in Smithport in 2000 than in 1985?

   _____

4. What could explain the change?

   _____

   _____

   _____

   _____

Notes for Home: Your child learned how to read a table to compare data.
Home Activity: Help your child make a table showing the high temperature every day for a week. Talk about any pattern you see.

Notes

Dear Family,

Your child is learning about the weather and how it can affect our lives. In the science chapter Weather, our class has learned about weather patterns, instruments scientists use to measure the weather, and different types of storms. They have also been studying the atmosphere, the blanket of air that surrounds Earth. Finally, we have looked at weather maps and discussed high and low temperatures.

In addition to learning about weather, the students have also learned many new vocabulary words. Help your child to make these words a part of his or her own vocabulary by using them when you talk together about the weather.

> weather
> atmosphere
> hurricane
> tornado
> blizzard

The following pages include activities that you and your child can do together. By participating in your child's education, you will help to bring the learning home.

Family Science Activity
Draw a Weather Report

Materials:

- newspaper, radio, or television
- white paper
- ruler
- colored pencils or markers

Steps

1. Watch or listen to a weather forecast together at home.

2. Discuss the weather conditions for today and the next few days. Will it be sunny, cloudy or rainy? Is a storm coming? Ask your child to read or listen for the barometric pressure. Discuss that if the barometric pressure is low, the weather may be cloudy or rainy. If the pressure is high, the skies may be clear.

3. Have your child pretend that he or she is a weather forecaster. Invite your child to draw three boxes on a piece of white paper, using a ruler.

4. Ask your child to draw a picture of the weather forecast for the following three days. This can be an imaginary forecast or based on the actual forecast.

5. Encourage your child to write in the **High Temperature** and **Low Temperature** for each day and whether the barometric pressure is high or low or changing.

6. Ask your child to explain the weather drawing to you and give a weather report. Display the weather forecast in your home.

Weather Words

Look for the words in the puzzle and circle them.

| atmosphere | blizzard | hurricane |
| tornado | weather | |

```
H  U  R  R  I  C  A  N  E  W
V  Y  U  E  H  G  Y  V  B  E
B  D  T  O  R  N  A  D  O  A
L  B  P  R  K  M  X  G  I  T
I  O  R  D  A  S  T  M  U  H
Z  O  R  J  C  P  R  L  Y  E
N  N  V  L  K  V  J  Q  R  R
A  T  M  O  S  P  H  E  R  E
R  G  V  T  O  A  S  E  W  R
D  I  S  E  H  M  A  E  W  E
```

Extreme Weather

Hurricanes, tornadoes, and blizzards can bring strong rain, winds, or snow. Read the words in the box and write them where they belong in the table.

| snow | storm | funnel |
| oceans | Strong | waves |

Hurricanes	Tornadoes	Blizzards
Huge storms that form over _____	Spinning _____ shaped columns of air	A winter _____
Heavy rain, strong winds, and huge _____	_____ winds	Blowing _____
_____ in the ocean		

Read the clues. Choose a word to answer each riddle.

rock	**metamorphic rock**	**igneous rock**
mineral	**sedimentary rock**	**decay**
soil	**nutrient**	**loam**

1. Granite is an example. It forms deep underground. It needs heat to form. What is it? _____

2. When they die, plants and animals do this. It means to break down into bits. What is it? _____

3. It covers most of the land on Earth. It is made up of bits of rock and dead plant and animal matter. It is a home to earthworms. What is it? _____

4. It is a natural material. It has never been living. Every rock contains at least one. What is it? _____

5. Heat and pressure made it what it is today. Its name means "changes form." Slate is an example. What is it?

   _____

6. It is a kind of soil. Plants grow well in it. It holds lots of water. It is a mixture. What is it? _____

7. It forms in layers. It might contain fossils. It can tell a "story" about how life has changed over time. What is it?

   _____

8. A mountain is mostly this. It is solid and nonliving. It contains one or more minerals. It can be placed in one of three main groups. What is it? _____

9. It is a material that plants take from soil. It helps plants grow. It might come from a mineral or decaying plants and animals. What is it? _____

Notes for Home: Your child learned the vocabulary terms for Chapter 7.
Home Activity: Have your child cut out magazine pictures or draw pictures that illustrate the vocabulary words. Make up sentences together that use the words.

Compare and Contrast

Read the magazine article and look at the pictures. How are rocks and soil alike and different?

Rocks and Soil

The solid surface of Earth is covered with rocks and soil. Rocks are made of one or more minerals. Minerals are natural nonliving materials. Rocks may be large or small, but they are solid and hard to break. When rocks break down, soil can start to form. Soil is a loose mix of tiny bits of rock and material from dead plants and animals. Water will soak up into soil, but it runs off of rock.

Apply It!
Use the graphic organizer on the next page to compare rocks with soil.

© Pearson Education, Inc.

Name _____

Rocks   Alike   **Soil**
Different   Different

Notes for Home: Your child learned about the skill of comparing and contrasting.
Home Activity: With your child make your own Venn diagram comparing and
contrasting two familiar things, such as two pets or two favorite foods.

Notes

Lesson 1: How do rocks form?

Before You Read Lesson 1

Read each statement below. Place a check mark in the circle to indicate whether you agree or disagree with the statement.

	Agree	Disagree
1. Rocks are made of one or more minerals.	○	○
2. Igneous rock forms in layers.	○	○
3. Fossils are usually found in metamorphic rock.	○	○

After You Read Lesson 1

Reread each statement above. If the lesson supports your choice, place a check mark in the *Correct* circle. Then explain how the text supports your choice. If the lesson does not support your choice, place a check mark in the *Incorrect* circle. Then explain why your choice is wrong.

	Correct	Incorrect
1. _____ _____	○	○
2. _____ _____	○	○
3. _____ _____	○	○

Notes for Home: Your child has completed a pre/post inventory of key concepts in the lesson.
Home Activity: Gather stones and sort them into groups according to similarities. Use the words *color, texture,* and *minerals* to describe the rock groups.

Name _____

Reviewing Terms: Matching

Match each description with the correct word or phrase. Write the letter on the line next to each description.

_____ 1. any solid, nonliving material made of one or more mineral

_____ 2. a natural material that forms from nonliving matter

_____ 3. a rock that forms from a mixture of melted material and gases

_____ 4. a rock made of layers that are cemented together

_____ 5. a rock that has been changed by heat and pressure

a. sedimentary rock

b. igneous rock

c. rock

d. mineral

e. metamorphic rock

Reviewing Concepts: True or False

Write **T** (True) or **F** (False) on the line before each statement.

_____ 6. All rocks have the same texture and grain size.

_____ 7. Fossils are most often found in metamorphic rock.

_____ 8. Igneous rock can come from volcanoes.

Applying Concepts: Compare and Contrast

Use complete sentences to answer question 9. (2 points)

9. Name one way in which sedimentary, igneous, and metamorphic rocks are similar and one way in which they are different.

_____

_____

_____

© Pearson Education, Inc.

Workbook

Lesson 2: What are minerals?

Before You Read Lesson 2

Read each statement below. Place a check mark in the circle to indicate whether you agree or disagree with the statement.

	Agree	Disagree
1. Minerals are identified using only their color.	○	○
2. You have used several minerals today.	○	○
3. Most foods except for vegetables contain minerals.	○	○

After You Read Lesson 2

Reread each statement above. If the lesson supports your choice, place a check mark in the *Correct* circle. Then explain how the text supports your choice. If the lesson does not support your choice, place a check mark in the *Incorrect* circle. Then explain why your choice is wrong.

	Correct	Incorrect
1. _____ _____	○	○
2. _____ _____	○	○
3. _____ _____	○	○

 Notes for Home: Your child has completed a pre/post inventory of key concepts in the lesson.
Home Activity: List some minerals, such as copper, quartz, graphite, and iron. Go on a household search for products that contain one or more of these minerals.

© Pearson Education, Inc.

Name _____

Reviewing Concepts: Sentence Completion

Complete the sentence with the correct word or phrase.

_____ 1. When a mineral is rubbed on a rough surface, it leaves a _____. (streak, luster)

_____ 2. Pearly, silky, greasy, and dull are ways to describe a mineral's _____. (luster, hardness)

_____ 3. _____ is the hardest mineral. (Talc, Diamond)

_____ 4. Minerals are found in _____ of the things people use every day. (many, few)

_____ 5. _____ is a mineral that helps bones form. (Copper, Calcium)

_____ 6. The mineral fluorite is found in _____. (steel, toothpaste)

_____ 7. The mineral halite is known as _____. (lead, table salt)

_____ 8. Almost _____ foods contain minerals. (all, no)

Writing

Use complete sentences to answer question 9. (2 points)

9. Name two minerals and tell how each one is used by the human body.

_____

_____

_____

Lesson 3: Why is soil important?

Before You Read Lesson 3

Read each statement below. Place a check mark in the circle to indicate whether you agree or disagree with the statement.

	Agree	Disagree
1. Soil is made of decaying plants and animals.	O	O
2. The top layer of soil is called topsoil.	O	O
3. Good soil does not contain living things.	O	O

After You Read Lesson 3

Reread each statement above. If the lesson supports your choice, place a check mark in the *Correct* circle. Then explain how the text supports your choice. If the lesson does not support your choice, place a check mark in the *Incorrect* circle. Then explain why your choice is wrong.

	Correct	Incorrect
1. _____	O	O
2. _____	O	O
3. _____	O	O

Notes for Home: Your child has completed a pre/post inventory of key concepts in the lesson.
Home Activity: Put sand and potting soil into plastic cups. Compare how much water each can hold. Draw a conclusion about which is better for plants.

© Pearson Education, Inc.

Reviewing Terms: Matching

Match each description with the correct word. Write the letter on the line next to each description.

_____ 1. a thin layer of loose material that covers Earth's land

_____ 2. the process of breaking down the remains of plants and animals

_____ 3. a kind of material released by decay

_____ 4. a soil with a mixture of sand, silt, clay, and humus

a. loam
b. nutrient
c. soil
d. decay

Reviewing Concepts: True or False

Write **T** (True) or **F** (False) on the line before each statement.

_____ 5. It takes about ten years for nature to rebuild lost topsoil.

_____ 6. Topsoil is the bottom layer of soil.

_____ 7. Clay has the smallest soil particle size.

_____ 8. Loam is soil that is good for growing plants.

Applying Concepts: Calculating

9. In a certain area the topsoil is 1.5 meters deep, the subsoil is 3.0 meters deep, and the bedrock is 6.0 meters deep. How many meters deep are all three soil layers together? Show your work. (2 points)

Minerals in Foods

Look at the table. A group of students looked at labels on food products at home. They recorded the number of foods they found that contain each mineral on the label.

Mineral	Calcium	Iron	Sodium	Potassium	Copper
Number of foods that have this mineral	32	24	51	12	8

Use the table to answer the questions.

1. Which mineral was found in the most foods?

   _____

2. Which mineral was found in the fewest foods?

   _____

3. The students looked at a total of 60 foods. How many foods in their sample were sodium free?

   _____

4. Which mineral was found in twice as many foods as potassium was found?

   _____

Notes for Home: Your child learned to read a table to compare data.
Home Activity: Help your child make a table showing how much calcium is in different dairy products. Compare which gives the most and least calcium per serving.

Notes

Dear Family,

Your child is learning about two of Earth's important resources. In the science chapter Rocks and Soil, our class has learned about how rocks are made, how rocks are different from one another, what soil is made of, and why soil is important. The children have also learned how and why fossils form in a certain kind of rock, and why minerals are such important materials in people's lives.

As the children learned about rocks and soil, they have also learned many new vocabulary words. Help your child to make these words a part of his or her own vocabulary by using them when you talk together about rocks and soil.

rock
mineral
igneous rock
sedimentary rock
metamorphic rock
soil
decay
nutrient
loam

The following pages include activities that you and your child can do together. By participating in your child's education, you will help to bring the learning home.

© Pearson Education, Inc.

Family Science Activity
Go on a Rock Hunt

Materials:

- sink or bowl with water
- newspaper
- coin

Steps

1. Go outside and look for rocks. Your child should collect at least three rocks to bring home. Help your child find rocks that look different from one another and are easy to carry. Wash the rocks at home to rid them of dirt.

2. Have your child look carefully at each rock. Ask him or her to describe the color(s) in each rock.

3. Have your child describe the texture of each rock—for example, is it smooth or rough? Does the rock have grains or layers in it?

4. Test each rock for the hardness of minerals in it. First, see if each rock easily scratches with a fingernail. Then, test to see if it scratches easily with a coin.

Talk About It

Discuss how the rocks are alike and different. Could any of them be **igneous rocks**—hard rock with grains? Could they be **sedimentary rocks**—softer rocks that form in layers? Could they be **metamorphic**—rocks that changed due to heat and pressure over a long period of time?

Vocabulary Puzzle

Circle the five words about soil in the puzzle.

ROCK	SOIL
NUTRIENT	LOAM
	DECAY

```
S  O  A  T  D  E  C  A  Y  P
O  O  N  R  O  E  B  M  E  T
I  O  N  U  T  R  I  E  N  T
L  E  T  A  L  O  A  M  U  S
S  O  I  C  A  C  S  I  G  N
D  E  C  O  K  K  S  O  I  M
```

A Story About Rocks

Use the letter code to spell the words in the story below.

LETTER CODE

1 = A	2 = C	3 = D	4 = E
5 = F	6 = G	7 = H	8 = I
9 = K	10 = L	11 = M	12 = N
13 = O	14 = P	15 = R	16 = S
17 = T	18 = U	19 = Y	

Edwin has a piece of

$\overline{11}$ $\overline{4}$ $\overline{17}$ $\overline{1}$ $\overline{11}$ $\overline{13}$ $\overline{15}$ $\overline{14}$ $\overline{7}$ $\overline{8}$ $\overline{2}$ $\overline{15}$ $\overline{13}$ $\overline{2}$ $\overline{9}$.

1.

Sonya has a **2.** _____ in

$\overline{5}$ $\overline{13}$ $\overline{16}$ $\overline{16}$ $\overline{8}$ $\overline{10}$

Edwin and Sonya share a **4.**

$\overline{16}$ $\overline{4}$ $\overline{3}$ $\overline{8}$ $\overline{11}$ $\overline{4}$ $\overline{12}$ $\overline{17}$ $\overline{1}$ $\overline{15}$ $\overline{19}$ $\overline{15}$ $\overline{13}$ $\overline{2}$ $\overline{9}$.

3.

$\overline{11}$ $\overline{1}$ $\overline{6}$ $\overline{12}$ $\overline{4}$

$\overline{17}$. It comes from a **5.**

$\overline{11}$ $\overline{8}$ $\overline{12}$ $\overline{4}$ $\overline{15}$ $\overline{1}$ $\overline{10}$

found in **6.**

$\overline{8}$ $\overline{6}$ $\overline{12}$ $\overline{4}$ $\overline{13}$ $\overline{18}$ $\overline{16}$ $\overline{15}$ $\overline{13}$ $\overline{2}$ $\overline{9}$.

Workbook

Name _____

Choose a word to complete each sentence. Underline clues that helped you decide which word to use.

erosion	core	mantle	landforms
crust	lava	magma	weathering

1. The outside layer of Earth, called the _____, is made of rock.

2. Rock in the _____, or middle layer of Earth, is hot enough to flow.

3. Though it is hottest of all, the Earth's inner _____ is packed so tightly that it stays solid.

4. Mountains, hills, valleys, and beaches are examples of Earth's _____.

5. _____ is hot, melted rock that pushes up toward Earth's surface because it is full of gases.

6. When a volcano erupts, melted rock called _____ is forced out.

7. The action of _____ changes a boulder into a pebble over time.

8. Bits of rock can be picked up and carried by wind, water, and glaciers in a process known as _____.

Notes for Home: Your child learned the vocabulary terms for Chapter 8.
Home Activity: Use vocabulary words in sentences that you and your child make up. Then have your child draw pictures to illustrate the words.

Sequence

Read the science article.

Growing a Glacier

It takes many years to grow a glacier. First, in a very cold place, snow keeps piling up because it does not melt from year to year. Then top layers press down on lower layers, packing them together. Next, the weight changes bottom layers of snow into ice.

Finally, the force is so great it causes the glacier to move over the ground, scraping rocks and dirt as it goes.

© Pearson Education, Inc.

Apply It!

How does a glacier form? Write the steps in order on the graphic organizer.

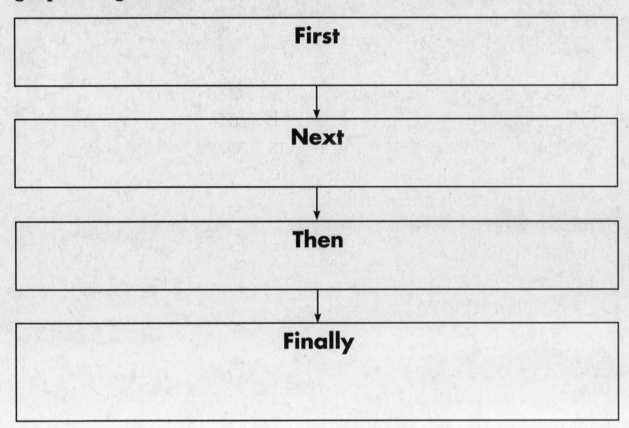

© Pearson Education, Inc.

Notes for Home: Your child learned how to sequence events.
Home Activity: Have your child draw a sequence chart showing how forces press on a glacier and cause it to move.

Notes

Lesson 1: What are Earth's layers?

Before You Read Lesson 1

Read each statement below. Place a check mark in the circle to indicate whether you agree or disagree with the statement.

	Agree	Disagree
1. The mantle of Earth moves like soft plastic.	○	○
2. The core of Earth is completely liquid.	○	○
3. A plateau is a high plain.	○	○

After You Read Lesson 1

Reread each statement above. If the lesson supports your choice, place a check mark in the *Correct* circle. Then explain how the text supports your choice. If the lesson does not support your choice, place a check mark in the *Incorrect* circle. Then explain why your choice is wrong.

	Correct	Incorrect
1. _____	○	○
_____		
2. _____	○	○
_____		
3. _____	○	○
_____		

Notes for Home: Your child has completed a pre/post inventory of key concepts in the lesson.
Home Activity: Take a walking tour or look at pictures of local landforms with your child. Discuss how these features might have been shaped by nature.

Name _____

Reviewing Terms: Sentence Completion

Complete each sentence with the correct word.

_____ 1. The _____ is the outer layer of Earth. (crust, core)

_____ 2. Earth's middle layer is the _____. (core, mantle)

_____ 3. The innermost layer of the Earth is the _____. (crust, core)

_____ 4. _____ are solid features on Earth's crust. (Oceans, Landforms)

Reviewing Concepts: Matching

Match each landform with the correct description. Write the letter on the line next to each description.

_____ 5. a large, mostly flat area   **a.** valley

_____ 6. the land next to the ocean   **b.** plain

_____ 7. a low, narrow area   **c.** coast

_____ 8. a high place   **d.** hill

Writing

Use complete sentences to answer question 9. (2 points)

9. Write a short paragraph that describes Earth's layers.

_____

_____

_____

_____

_____

© Pearson Education, Inc.

Lesson 2: What are volcanoes and earthquakes?

Before You Read Lesson 2

Read each statement below. Place a check mark in the circle to indicate whether you agree or disagree with the statement.

	Agree	Disagree
1. Lava hardens to form igneous rock.	○	○
2. Moving parts of Earth's crust cause earthquakes.	○	○
3. Earthquakes often happen along faults.	○	○

After You Read Lesson 2

Reread each statement above. If the lesson supports your choice, place a check mark in the *Correct* circle. Then explain how the text supports your choice. If the lesson does not support your choice, place a check mark in the *Incorrect* circle. Then explain why your choice is wrong.

	Correct	Incorrect
1. _____ _____	○	○
2. _____ _____	○	○
3. _____ _____	○	○

 Notes for Home: Your child has completed a pre/post inventory of key concepts in the lesson.
Home Activity: Ask your child to explain how earthquakes and volcanoes are related to the crust and mantle of Earth.

Reviewing Terms: Sentence Completion

Complete each sentence with the correct word.

_____ 1. _____ is hot, melted rock under the ground. (Lava, Magma)

_____ 2. Melted rock that has come out of a volcano is called _____. (lava, eruption)

Reviewing Concepts: True or False

Write **T** (True) or **F** (False) on the line before each statement.

_____ 3. Magma forms in Earth's core.

_____ 4. A volcano is an opening in Earth's crust.

_____ 5. When lava cools, it becomes sedimentary rock.

_____ 6. Magma collects underground in magma chambers.

_____ 7. Earthquake vibrations travel as waves.

_____ 8. The farther an earthquake is from a city, the more damage it causes there.

Applying Strategies: Sequence

Use complete sentences to answer question 9. (2 points)

9. Using the clue words in the sentences, write the steps of a volcanic eruption in the correct order.

Next, magma pushes up through cracks in Earth's crust.
First, magma forms deep in the Earth.
Finally, lava cools and hardens, forming igneous rock.
Then magma comes out of the volcano and is called lava.

_____

_____

_____

© Pearson Education, Inc.

Name _____

Lesson 3: What are weathering and erosion?

Before You Read Lesson 3

Read each statement below. Place a check mark in the circle to indicate whether you agree or disagree with the statement.

	Agree	Disagree
1. Erosion is caused mostly by wind.	○	○
2. Weathering causes rocks to break up.	○	○
3. Living things do not cause weathering.	○	○

After You Read Lesson 3

Reread each statement above. If the lesson supports your choice, place a check mark in the *Correct* circle. Then explain how the text supports your choice. If the lesson does not support your choice, place a check mark in the *Incorrect* circle. Then explain why your choice is wrong.

	Correct	Incorrect
1. _____	○	○
_____		
2. _____	○	○
_____		
3. _____	○	○
_____		

Notes for Home: Your child has completed a pre/post inventory of key concepts in the lesson.
Home Activity: Freeze an exact amount of water in a measuring cup and then remeasure it. Talk about how the increase in the volume of water when it freezes helps break up rocks.

Reviewing Terms: Matching

Match each description with the correct word. Write the letter on the line next to each description.

_____ 1. any action that breaks rocks   **a.** erosion
into smaller pieces   **b.** weathering

_____ 2. the movement of broken rocks
and Earth materials

Reviewing Concepts: Sentence Completion

Complete the sentence with the correct word or phrase.

_____ 3. Landforms _____ change. (always, never)

_____ 4. Plant's roots can cause _____. (weathering, erosion)

_____ 5. _____ makes water expand and crack rocks. (Freezing, Thawing)

_____ 6. Rainwater causes soil loss by _____. (erosion, gravity)

_____ 7. In dry areas like deserts, _____ causes most of the erosion. (wind, water)

_____ 8. A mudflow is caused by _____. (wind, gravity)

Applying Concepts: Comparing Numbers

9. Using the list below, tell what kind of rock is 10 times larger than a pebble. Explain how you know. (2 points)

<u>Sizes of Rocks</u>

Boulder	300 mm	Cobble	100 mm
Pebble	30 mm	Sand	1 mm

_____

_____

Name _____

Measuring an Earthquake

The Richter scale measures the strength of earthquakes. Very weak earthquakes have a number from 1 to 3. The strongest earthquakes measure 7 or 8 on the Richter scale.

Richter Magnitude	Effects	Number
Less than 2.0	Not felt	About 8,000 per day
2.0–2.9	Usually not felt	About 1,000 per day
3.0–3.9	Often felt, but rarely causes damage	49,000 per year
4.0–4.9	Not much damage likely	6,200 per year
5.0–5.9	Damage to poorly made buildings over a small area	800 per year
6.0–6.9	Property destroyed over an area up to 100 miles across	120 per year
7.0–7.9	Serious damage over a larger area	18 per year
8.0 or greater	Serious damage in areas several hundred miles across	1 per year

Use the table to answer the questions.

1. About how many earthquakes with a magnitude of 5.0 to 5.9 occur each year? _____

2. What effects can an earthquake with a magnitude of 6.0 to 6.9 have? _____

   _____

3. How would you describe the relationship of the size, or magnitude, of earthquakes and the number of earthquakes that occur each year? _____

   _____

Notes for Home: Your child learned how earthquake size and strength are measured.
Home Activity: Talk with your child about any earthquakes in your area. Visit a library or Web site to learn about what to do for safety during an earthquake.

Notes

Dear Family,

Your child is learning about the surface of the earth and ways in which it changes. In the science chapter Changes on Earth, our class has learned about Earth's layers and landforms. The children also learned about events that cause the surface of Earth to change—including volcanoes, earthquakes, weathering, and erosion.

As the children learned about how Earth changes, they have also learned many new vocabulary words. Help your child to make these words a part of his or her own vocabulary by using them when you talk together about Earth and the way in which it changes.

crust
mantle
core
landform
magma
lava
weathering
erosion

The following pages include activities that you and your child can do together. By participating in your child's education, you will help to bring the learning home.

Family Science Activity
Create a Landforms Poster

Materials
- old newspapers and magazines
- scissors
- paper
- glue or paste
- marker

Steps

1. With your child, look through old magazines or newspapers. Cut out photographs of scenes in nature.

2. If the photograph has a caption, read it with your child. Have your child point out different landforms in the photographs—such as mountains, plateaus, hills, valleys, lakes, streams, rivers, or oceans.

3. Have your child choose at least four photographs to organize in a poster that shows different landforms.

4. With your child, arrange the photographs on the large sheet of paper. Use the glue or paste to hold the photographs in place. (Leave some space for writing the title and a caption.)

5. Invite your child to write a title and short sentences telling about the photographs in the poster.

6. Ask you child to explain the poster to you. Then, display it in the home.

Vocabulary Riddles

Write the vocabulary word from the box that answers each riddle.

crust	mantle	core	magma

1. I am what you find inside an apple. I am the word

_____

2. I am what you find on the outside of a pie. I am the word

_____

3. The word "man" is part of me. I am the word

_____

4. I am a mother with a "g" in it. I am the word

_____

Word Puzzle

Use the words below to complete the puzzle about Earth. Write one letter in each box.

earthquake	erosion	lava
volcano	weathering	

w

n

e

v

v

a

Name _____

Circle the letter of the answer that best completes the meaning of the boldfaced word.

1. **Natural resources** are materials from the Earth that living things need, such as ___.
   A. air
   B. water
   C. minerals
   D. all of the above

2. Some resources are **renewable**, which means that they ___.
   A. can be replaced
   B. cannot be replaced
   C. are not needed
   D. are needed more than other resources

3. **Nonrenewable resources**, such as oil, coal, and iron, must be used carefully because ___.
   A. they are dangerous
   B. we have very little of these resources
   C. Earth cannot replace them
   D. they pollute the Earth

4. **Conservation** will help people in the long run because it ___.
   A. helps us find new resources
   B. prevents the waste of resources
   C. purifies dirty water
   D. blows away soil

5. To **recycle** resources, you must ___.
   A. change them so they can be used again
   B. use them over and over
   C. throw them away
   D. use less of them

 Notes for Home: Your child learned the vocabulary terms for Chapter 9.
Home Activity: Use vocabulary words as you and your child put away groceries and other items. Discuss the resources used to make these products and how you can conserve and recycle.

🎯 Compare and Contrast

Read the science article.

Energy

We burn a lot of coal to produce energy. In fact, coal furnishes 22 percent of the energy used in the United States. Mostly, coal energy is changed into electricity or used to run steam engines. However, burning coal releases pollution into the air. To get coal, we must mine it from the ground, which is dangerous for workers. Also, one day, we will run out of coal.

Solar energy is energy from the Sun. People capture it using panels or cells. These devices change the solar energy into heat energy or electric energy. This energy supply is clean and unlimited. However, it takes time to collect enough solar energy to use, and the devices used to collect it make it more expensive than other forms of energy. Also, clouds and night take away the source of this energy.

Name _____

Apply It!

Fill in the graphic organizer. Write how solar energy and energy from burning coal are alike and different.

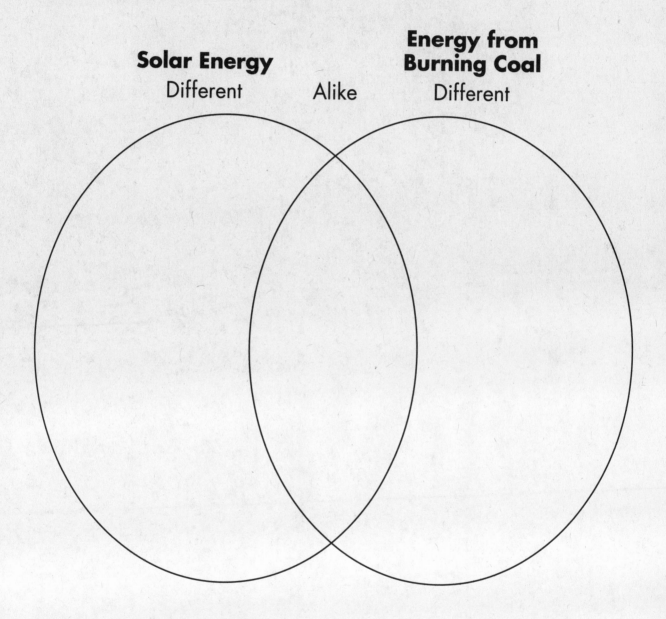

Solar Energy

Different   Alike   **Energy from Burning Coal**

Different

© Pearson Education, Inc.

Notes for Home: Your child learned how to compare and contrast.
Home Activity: With your child, investigate what energy source(s) are used to provide your electricity. How does the power company avoid polluting the air?

Notes

Lesson 1: What are resources?

Before You Read Lesson 1

Read each statement below. Place a check mark in the circle to indicate whether you agree or disagree with the statement.

	Agree	Disagree
1. To renew the resource of trees, you plant new ones.	○	○
2. Fuels such as oil, natural gas, and coal are renewable resources.	○	○
3. Sunlight is a nonrenewable resource.	○	○

After You Read Lesson 1

Reread each statement above. If the lesson supports your choice, place a check mark in the *Correct* circle. Then explain how the text supports your choice. If the lesson does not support your choice, place a check mark in the *Incorrect* circle. Then explain why your choice is wrong.

	Correct	Incorrect
1. _____	○	○
_____		
2. _____	○	○
_____		
3. _____	○	○
_____		

Notes for Home: Your child has completed a pre/post inventory of key concepts in the lesson.
Home Activity: With your child, go on a search to identify products and furnishings in your home that are made from trees, iron ore, oil, or coal.

Reviewing Terms: Matching

Match each description with the correct phrase. Write the letter on the line next to each description.

_____ 1. important materials from Earth that living things need

_____ 2. resources that can be replaced in a fairly short time

_____ 3. resources that cannot be replaced

a. renewable resources

b. natural resources

c. nonrenewable resources

Reviewing Concepts: True or False

Write **T** (True) or **F** (False) on the line before each statement.

_____ 4. Wood is a natural resource.

_____ 5. Trees are a nonrenewable resource.

_____ 6. Ores are rocks that contain metals or minerals.

_____ 7. Iron is a renewable resource.

_____ 8. Sunlight is a resource that cannot get used up.

Writing

Use complete sentences to answer question 9. (2 points)

9. Describe one natural resource and explain how it is used by people.

_____

_____

_____

_____

© Pearson Education, Inc.

Lesson 2: How can we protect our resources?

Before You Read Lesson 2

Read each statement below. Place a check mark in the circle to indicate whether you agree or disagree with the statement.

	Agree	Disagree
1. When you conserve resources, you waste them.	○	○
2. Most of our trash is paper.	○	○
3. Landfills are large areas where trash is buried.	○	○

After You Read Lesson 2

Reread each statement above. If the lesson supports your choice, place a check mark in the *Correct* circle. Then explain how the text supports your choice. If the lesson does not support your choice, place a check mark in the *Incorrect* circle. Then explain why your choice is wrong.

	Correct	Incorrect
1. _____ _____	○	○
2. _____ _____	○	○
3. _____ _____	○	○

Notes for Home: Your child has completed a pre/post inventory of key concepts in the lesson.
Home Activity: List ways you and your child could conserve resources such as fuels. For example, you might walk to school together rather than use a car.

Reviewing Terms: Sentence Completion

Complete the sentence with the correct word.

_____ 1. _____ is the wise use of any natural resource. (Compost, Conservation)

Reviewing Concepts: Sentence Completion

Complete each sentence with the correct word.

_____ 2. You can conserve water by using _____ of it. (more, less)

_____ 3. Wetlands can _____ water. (clean, compost)

_____ 4. Wind and water can cause soil _____. (conservation, erosion)

_____ 5. Decay can turn yard clippings into _____. (water, compost)

_____ 6. A _____ is a place where trash is buried. (landfill, wetland)

_____ 7. Smoke from burning garbage must be _____ before it is released into the air. (cleaned, conserved)

_____ 8. _____ landfill space would be needed if people made smaller amounts of trash. (Less, More)

Applying Strategies: Compare and Contrast

Use complete sentences to answer question 9. (2 points)

9. What is one way that conserving soil and conserving water are similar actions? What is one way they are different?

_____

_____

_____

Lesson 3: What are ways to use resources again?

Before You Read Lesson 3

Read each statement below. Place a check mark in the circle to indicate whether you agree or disagree with the statement.

	Agree	Disagree
1. When you recycle something, you change it so that it can be used again.	○	○
2. Glass can only be recycled once.	○	○
3. The three *R*'s for protecting resources are *renewal, refuse,* and *resource*.	○	○

After You Read Lesson 3

Reread each statement above. If the lesson supports your choice, place a check mark in the *Correct* circle. Then explain how the text supports your choice. If the lesson does not support your choice, place a check mark in the *Incorrect* circle. Then explain why your choice is wrong.

	Correct	Incorrect
1. _____ _____	○	○
2. _____ _____	○	○
3. _____ _____	○	○

 Notes for Home: Your child has completed a pre/post inventory of key concepts in the lesson.
Home Activity: Begin a family reuse program in which everyone tries to find ways to reuse things the family no longer needs or wants. For example, an old towel could be torn up for use as rags.

Reviewing Terms: Sentence Completion

Complete the sentence with the correct word.

_____ 1. To _____ is to make something into a new product so it can be used again. (reuse, recycle)

Reviewing Concepts: True or False

Write **T** (True) or **F** (False) on the line before each statement.

_____ 2. Reusing things is one way to conserve resources.

_____ 3. Metal, glass, paper, and plastic are materials that can be recycled.

_____ 4. In reusing, a new product is made.

_____ 5. Reusing things to conserve resources is a new idea.

_____ 6. Recycling glass does not save energy.

_____ 7. Buying products made from recycled materials helps conserve resources.

_____ 8. Reduce, reuse, and recycle are three ways to care for the Earth.

Applying Strategies: Calculating

9. People recycle 70 kilograms of cardboard for every 100 kilograms produced. If 500 kilograms of cardboard are produced, how many kilograms will be recycled? Show your work. (2 points)

© Pearson Education, Inc.

Disappearing Forests

The graph shows how much tropical forest has been lost in just 30 years in three regions of the world as well as in the world overall.

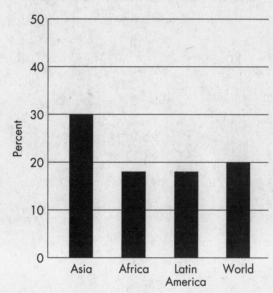

Percent of Tropical Forest Cleared Between 1960 and 1990

Use the graph to answer these questions.

1. What percent of Asia's tropical forests was cut down between 1960 and 1990? _____

2. The bar for *World* shows the average percent of tropical forest cut down in all regions. What percent of the world's tropical forests was cut down between 1960 and 1990?

   _____

3. What conclusion can you draw from what this graph shows? _____

   _____

   _____

Notes for Home: Your child learned to read a bar graph.
Home Activity: Together count the number of food cans, boxes, and packages in your kitchen and make a bar graph that shows this data. Then ask your child questions about the bar graph.

Notes

Dear Family,

Your child is learning about Earth's natural resources. In the science chapter Natural Resources, our class has learned how we use natural resources—those that can be replaced in a short period of time (**renewable resources**) and those that cannot be replaced (**nonrenewable resources**). The children also learned about conservation and recycling of natural resources.

As the children learned about natural resources, they have also learned many new vocabulary words. Help your child to make these words a part of his or her own vocabulary by using them when you talk together about Earth and its natural resources.

natural resource
renewable resource
nonrenewable resource
conservation
recycle

The following pages include activities that you and your child can do together. By participating in your child's education, you will help to bring the learning home.

Family Science Activity
Recycle a Paper Grocery Bag

Help your child learn how natural resources may be recycled by making a kite from a paper grocery bag.

Materials:

- paper grocery bag
- scissors
- two sticks
- glue or stapler
- spool of string
- yarn or ribbon (optional)

Steps

1. Make a large rectangle from the paper grocery bag. To do this, use scissors to cut around the bottom and then up one side of the bag.

2. Make a diamond shape from the rectangle by folding the ends to a point. Use glue or staples to hold this diamond shape.

3. With the two sticks, form a "t" shape. Tie the "t" shape with a piece of the string.

4. Glue or staple the "t" onto the kite so that the "t" reaches from corner to corner across the diamond shape. (You may also use string to tie the "t" to the four corners of the kite.

5. Tie string from the spool to the center of the "t" with a strong knot. (When you fly the kite, you hold onto the spool and either let out the string or reel it in.)

6. If you like, decorate the kite by attaching pieces of yarn or ribbon that will blow in the breeze when you fly the kite.

Recycling

When you **recycle** something, you use a material again to make something else. All the pairs of things below are examples of recycling except for one pair. Circle the one pair that is **not** an example of recycling.

Before Recycling ———▶ **After Recyling**

1. aluminum can ———▶ toy truck

2. newspaper ———▶ envelope

3. rubber tire ———▶ raincoat and boots

4. plastic bowl ———▶ dictionary

5. glass bottle ———▶ glass bracelet

Fun Fact

Every day, businesses in the United States throw away a lot of paper. How much? Well, enough paper to circle our planet 20 times!

Name _____

Circle the letter of the answer that best tells what the boldfaced word means.

1. Everything around you is made of **matter**—even the air.
   A. simple things
   B. anything that has mass and takes up space

2. Use your senses to discover the **properties** of a thing.
   A. true statements   B. qualities you can observe

3. As you blow up a balloon, air inside it has more and more **pressure.**
   A. pushing force   B. volume

4. The smallest particles of an **element** keep all the properties of the element.
   A. tiny piece
   B. substance made of one kind of particle

5. Gold is made up only of **atoms** of gold, but one **atom** of gold would be far too small to see.
   A. smallest unit of an element
   B. smallest particle possible

6. Every element has its place on the **periodic table.**
   A. list of matter   B. orderly arrangement of elements

7. You can measure an object's **mass** with a scale or a balance.
   A. amount of matter   B. size

8. When you measure milk for a cake, you measure its **volume.**
   A. weight   B. space taken up

9. Two balls of the same size that weigh different amounts have a different **density.**
   A. volume   B. amount of matter per unit of space

10. A plastic lid has more **buoyancy** than a rock.
    A. ability to float   B. ability to sink

 Notes for Home: Your child learned the vocabulary terms for Chapter 10.
Home Activity: Have your child use pictures and other graphics in Chapter 10 to explain the meanings of the vocabulary words.

© Pearson Education, Inc.

Cause and Effect

Read the science article.

How Ice Cream Melts

A solid can change into a liquid. For example, on a hot day ice cream melts quickly. What causes this to happen? The ice cream absorbs heat energy from the sun. This adds energy to the tiny particles of which the ice cream is made. Then the particles can move around more freely. As a result, the solid ice cream becomes a liquid that can be poured.

Apply It!

Fill in the graphic organizer. Write three causes and an effect from the article.

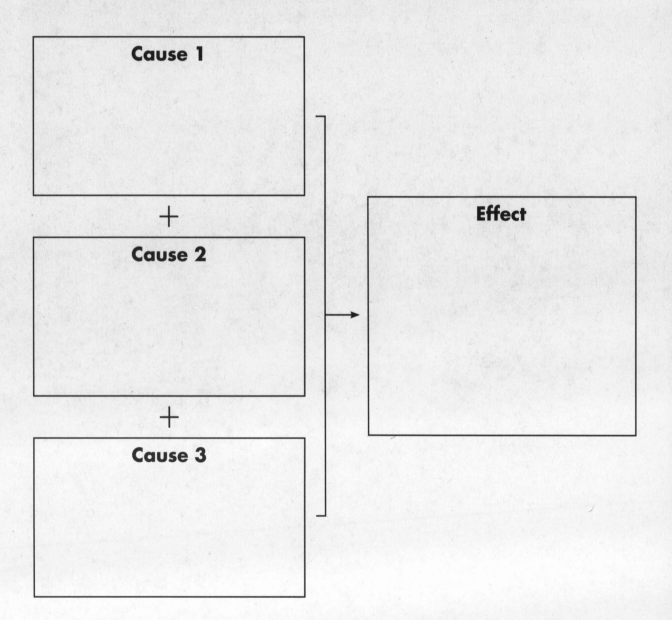

© Pearson Education, Inc.

Notes for Home: Your child learned how to identify causes and effects.
Home Activity: With your child, name various things that can change from a solid to a liquid by adding heat. (Some examples include ice, chocolate, iron, and gold.)

Notes

Lesson 1: How can we describe matter?

Before You Read Lesson 1

Read each statement below. Place a check mark in the circle to indicate whether you agree or disagree with the statement.

	Agree	Disagree
1. All matter is solid or liquid.	○	○
2. The particles of a solid stay in place.	○	○
3. In an element, all particles are one kind.	○	○

After You Read Lesson 1

Reread each statement above. If the lesson supports your choice, place a check mark in the *Correct* circle. Then explain how the text supports your choice. If the lesson does not support your choice, place a check mark in the *Incorrect* circle. Then explain why your choice is wrong.

	Correct	Incorrect
1. _____	○	○
_____		
2. _____	○	○
_____		
3. _____	○	○
_____		

Notes for Home: Your child has completed a pre/post inventory of key concepts in the lesson.
Home Activity: Have your child choose a solid, a liquid, and a gas (air in a balloon) available at home. Demonstrate the properties of each kind of matter.

Reviewing Terms: Matching

Match each description with the correct word or phrase. Write the letter on the line next to each description.

_____ 1. anything that takes up space and has weight

_____ 2. something you can observe about matter

_____ 3. pushing by particles in matter

_____ 4. matter made of a single type of particle

_____ 5. the smallest particle of an element that has the properties of the element

_____ 6. a way of arranging elements based on their properties

a. property
b. periodic table
c. pressure
d. element
e. atom
f. matter

Reviewing Concepts: Sentence Completion

Complete the sentence with the correct word.

_____ 7. Matter that is a _____ does not change its shape. (solid, gas)

_____ 8. A _____ expands and fills all the space available. (gas, liquid)

Writing

Use complete sentences to answer question 9. (2 points)

9. Describe one of the states of matter. Then give one example of something you use every day that is found in that state of matter.

_____

_____

Name _____

Lesson 2: How are properties of matter measured?

Before You Read Lesson 2

Read each statement below. Place a check mark in the circle to indicate whether you agree or disagree with the statement.

	Agree	Disagree
1. An object's mass is its weight.	○	○
2. Volume is measured in liters.	○	○
3. Objects that sink are more dense than water.	○	○

After You Read Lesson 2

Reread each statement above. If the lesson supports your choice, place a check mark in the *Correct* circle. Then explain how the text supports your choice. If the lesson does not support your choice, place a check mark in the *Incorrect* circle. Then explain why your choice is wrong.

	Correct	Incorrect
1. _____ _____	○	○
2. _____ _____	○	○
3. _____ _____	○	○

Notes for Home: Your child has completed a pre/post inventory of key concepts in the lesson.
Home Activity: Have your child use a measuring cup to measure the volume of different-sized glasses of water or milk.

Reviewing Terms: Sentence Completion

Complete each sentence with the correct word.

_____ 1. The amount of matter in an object is its _____.
(mass, volume)

_____ 2. An object's _____ is the amount of space the
object takes up. (density, volume)

_____ 3. _____ is the amount of matter in a certain
amount of space. (Mass, Density)

_____ 4. _____ is the property of matter that describes
how well an object floats. (Buoyancy, Volume)

Reviewing Concepts: True or False

Write **T** (True) or **F** (False) on the line before each statement.

_____ 5. Volume is measured using a balance.

_____ 6. To compare the density of two solid objects, you
need to know their masses and their volumes.

_____ 7. Metric rulers are used to measure length.

_____ 8. Magnifying glasses and hand lenses are used to
observe very small objects.

Applying Strategies: Cause and Effect

Use complete sentences to answer question 9. (2 points)

9. What is the effect of placing an object with a greater
density than water in a bucket of water?

_____

_____

_____

Name _____

Measuring and Comparing Properties

Use the pictures to answer the questions.

A   B   C

1. What property is being measured in drawings A and B?

   _____

2. How much longer is the finger than the toe?

   _____

3. What property is being measured in drawing C?

   _____

4. How will this property change if the milk is poured into
   a glass? _____

Notes for Home: Your child learned about measuring length and volume and
comparing measurements.
Home Activity: Put water in a measuring cup and line up different-sized glasses.
Have your child predict which ones will hold all the water. Check the predictions.

Notes

Dear Family,

Your child is learning about **matter**—that is, things we can see, smell, or touch along with many things our senses cannot experience directly. In the science chapter Matter and Its Properties, our class has learned how to observe and describe matter by some of its properties, or characteristics. The children also learned about ways to measure properties of matter.

As the children learned about matter, they have also learned many new vocabulary words. Help your child to make these words a part of his or her own vocabulary by using them when you talk together about matter and its properties.

> matter
> property
> pressure
> element
> atom
> periodic table
> mass
> volume
> density
> buoyancy

The following pages include activities that you and your child can do together. By participating in your child's education, you will help to bring the learning home.

Family Science Activity
Play the "Will It Float?" Game

Your child will discover which objects float or sink in water and learn about matter from this simple game. Objects that are denser than water will sink. Objects that are not as dense as water will float.

Materials

- large measuring cup or bowl
- a cork or other small object that floats in water
- five objects smaller than the measuring cup or bowl
- paper and pencil

Steps

1. Choose a large measuring cup or bowl and fill it 2/3 to 3/4 full of water.
2. Have your child collect five objects to place in the water.
3. First, place the cork or another object that floats in the water. Discuss with your child that the cork floats.
3. Have your child describe one of the other objects. Is it larger or smaller than the cork? Does it feel heavier or lighter?
4. Ask your child to put other objects in the water, one at a time.
5. Encourage your child to make a chart: "Objects that Float" and "Objects that Sink."

Talk About It

Discuss that the cork floated because it was not as dense as water. What other objects floated? Which objects sank? Why do some things sink in water while other things float?

Vocabulary Word Scramble

To complete each sentence below, unscramble the letters to find the vocabulary word.

Vocabulary Words

matter	property	pressure	element
atom	periodic table	mass	
density	buoyancy	volume	

1. A book has more **nsdyite** _____ than a bubble.

2. Nothing is smaller than an **toma** _____.

3. The smoothness of a banana peel is a _____ of the banana **erprytop** _____.

4. A balloon has **uybaycon** _____ because it floats on water.

5. A pencil is **tamret** _____ that takes up space and has weight.

© Pearson Education, Inc.

Continue the game from page 2.

6. The **temenle** _____ in silver is different than the one in iron.

7. This cup will measure the **eluvmo** _____ of tomato juice.

8. How much **sams** _____ does your computer have?

9. The teacher showed us a chart of the **idcorpie ealtb** _____.

10. A lot of **esperurs** _____ made the ball feel hard.

Fun Fact

Can you answer this question: What weighs more, a pound of steel or a pound of feathers?

Name _____

Write the words in the diagram where they belong. Then add examples for three vocabulary words.

| physical change | mixture | chemical change | solution |

Changes in Matter

Does not become a new kind of matter in a

_____

Does become a new kind of matter in a

_____

Pieces of matter are combined in a

_____

Examples: baking cookie dough making cheese

_____

_____

Examples: coins mixed nuts

_____

_____

One kind of matter is dissolved in another kind in a

_____

Examples: salt water, soda

_____

_____

Notes for Home: Your child learned the vocabulary terms for Chapter 11.
Home Activity: With your child, create chemical and physical changes involving mixtures, such as sand and rocks, lemonade, or cookies. Talk about how each mixture changes.

© Pearson Education, Inc.

Cause and Effect

Read the science article.

How Wood Burns

What happens to wood when it burns? It gives off heat, of course. It also goes through a chemical change. The wood combines with oxygen and changes to new substances. Some of the wood turns into gases that go into the atmosphere. Much of the wood is changed to ashes. When you put out a campfire, you are looking at a chemical change!

Name _____

Apply It!

Fill in the graphic organizer. Write a cause and three effects from the article.

Cause	Effects
	1.
	2.
	3.

© Pearson Education, Inc.

Notes for Home: Your child learned how to identify causes and effects.
Home Activity: With your child, safely build and light a small fire in a fireplace, or burn a stick of incense. Observe what happens to the wood or incense.

Notes

Lesson 1: What are physical changes in matter?

Before You Read Lesson 1

Read each statement below. Place a check mark in the circle to indicate whether you agree or disagree with the statement.

	Agree	Disagree
1. A physical change means matter changes form.	○	○
2. Melting is not a physical change.	○	○
3. Ice and water contain the same particles.	○	○

After You Read Lesson 1

Reread each statement above. If the lesson supports your choice, place a check mark in the *Correct* circle. Then explain how the text supports your choice. If the lesson does not support your choice, place a check mark in the *Incorrect* circle. Then explain why your choice is wrong.

	Correct	Incorrect
1. _____ _____	○	○
2. _____ _____	○	○
3. _____ _____	○	○

Notes for Home: Your child has completed a pre/post inventory of key concepts in the lesson.
Home Activity: Have your child help make dinner. Point out physical changes, such as cutting up fruit or salting potatoes.

Reviewing Terms: Matching

Match each description with the correct phrase. Write the letter on the line next to each description.

_____ 1. when matter changes the way it looks without becoming a new kind of matter

      a. states of matter

      b. physical change

_____ 2. the forms that matter can take

Reviewing Concepts: True or False

Write **T** (True) or **F** (False) on the line before each statement.

_____ 3. After a physical change there is a new kind of matter.

_____ 4. A change from one state of matter to another is a physical change.

_____ 5. A change in temperature can cause a change of state.

_____ 6. The particles in water move more when it is a solid than they do when it is a liquid.

_____ 7. When water evaporates, it becomes a new kind of matter.

_____ 8. When water freezes, the amount of water stays the same.

Analyzing Strategies: Cause and Effect

Use a complete sentence to answer question 9. (2 points)

9. What is the effect of placing a block of ice in the hot sunshine?

_____

_____

Name _____

Lesson 2: What are some ways to combine matter?

Before You Read Lesson 2

Read each statement below. Place a check mark in the circle to indicate whether you agree or disagree with the statement.

	Agree	Disagree
1. A mixture contains two or more kinds of matter.	○	○
2. A solution is a kind of mixture.	○	○
3. Solutions cannot be separated.	○	○

After You Read Lesson 2

Reread each statement above. If the lesson supports your choice, place a check mark in the *Correct* circle. Then explain how the text supports your choice. If the lesson does not support your choice, place a check mark in the *Incorrect* circle. Then explain why your choice is wrong.

	Correct	Incorrect
1. _____ _____	○	○
2. _____ _____	○	○
3. _____ _____	○	○

Notes for Home: Your child has completed a pre/post inventory of key concepts in the lesson.
Home Activity: With your child, make a mixture of sand and pebbles. Choose a method of separating the mixture. Repeat with a mixture of sand and salt.

Name _____

Reviewing Terms: Sentence Completion

Complete each sentence with the correct word.

_____ 1. Two or more kinds of matter placed together form a _____. (gas, mixture)

_____ 2. A _____ is formed when one substance dissolves in another. (solution, solid)

Reviewing Concepts: Sentence Completion

Complete the sentence with the correct word or phrase.

_____ 3. A pile of pennies, nickels, and dimes is a _____. (mixture, solution)

_____ 4. When a mixture is formed, each kind of matter _____. (changes, stays the same)

_____ 5. A mixture of sand and small iron pieces can be separated using a _____. (strainer, magnet)

_____ 6. Salt can be separated out of a salt water solution by _____. (straining, boiling)

_____ 7. Dissolving is a _____. (change in state, physical change)

_____ 8. When salt dissolves in water, the amount of salt _____. (decreases, stays the same)

Applying Strategies: Calculating

9. A mixture was formed with 220 grams of marbles, 52 grams of sand, and 127 grams of iron pieces. What was the total mass of the mixture? Show your work. (2 points)

Lesson 3: What are chemical changes in matter?

Before You Read Lesson 3

Read each statement below. Place a check mark in the circle to indicate whether you agree or disagree with the statement.

	Agree	Disagree
1. Cooking food causes chemical changes.	○	○
2. Chemical changes always happen quickly.	○	○
3. Digesting food is a chemical change.	○	○

After You Read Lesson 3

Reread each statement above. If the lesson supports your choice, place a check mark in the *Correct* circle. Then explain how the text supports your choice. If the lesson does not support your choice, place a check mark in the *Incorrect* circle. Then explain why your choice is wrong.

	Correct	Incorrect
1. _____ _____	○	○
2. _____ _____	○	○
3. _____ _____	○	○

Notes for Home: Your child has completed a pre/post inventory of key concepts in the lesson.
Home Activity: As you and your child read a library book, list the chemical changes that are happening in the illustrations, such as burning gasoline or cooking food.

Reviewing Terms: Sentence Completion

Complete the sentence with the correct phrase.

_____ 1. A _____ happens when one kind of matter changes into a different kind of matter. (chemical change, physical change)

Reviewing Concepts: Matching

Some changes in matter are chemical changes. Some changes are not. For each change in matter in the left column, choose the correct description in the right column. You can use each answer more than once.

_____ 2. baking cookie dough
_____ 3. slicing a loaf of bread
_____ 4. iron rusting
_____ 5. ice melting
_____ 6. wood burning
_____ 7. paper tearing
_____ 8. water evaporating

a. chemical change
b. not a chemical change

Writing

Use complete sentences to answer question 9. (2 points)

9. Write a paragraph that describes one chemical change that is a part of your everyday life.

_____

_____

_____

_____

Name _____

A Closer Look at Mixtures

Use the pictures to answer the questions.

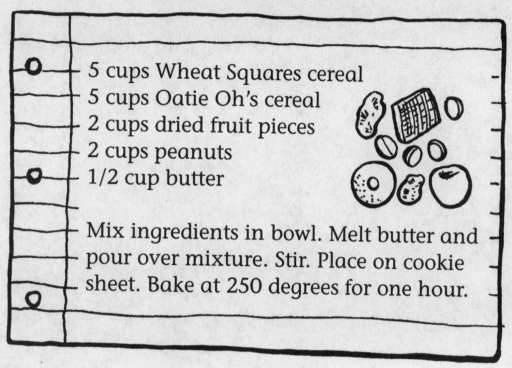

5 cups Wheat Squares cereal
5 cups Oatie Oh's cereal
2 cups dried fruit pieces
2 cups peanuts
1/2 cup butter

Mix ingredients in bowl. Melt butter and pour over mixture. Stir. Place on cookie sheet. Bake at 250 degrees for one hour.

1. What is the total volume of the dried parts of this mixture?
   _____

2. How many more cups of cereal are included than cups of fruit and nuts? _____

3. You double the amount of peanuts in the mix. How much more fruit and nuts do you have than Wheat Squares in your mix? _____

Notes for Home: Your child learned about comparing quantity or volume of ingredients in a mixture.
Home Activity: Help your child create a mixture such as fruit salad. Measure the amount of each part of the mixture.

Notes

Dear Family,

Your child is learning about physical changes and chemical changes in matter. In the science chapter Changes in Matter, our class has learned about the three states of matter (solid, liquid, gas), how physical changes affect matter, and different ways in which materials mix together. The children also learned about chemical changes that are part of their everyday lives.

As the children learned about changes in matter, they have also learned many new vocabulary words. Help your child to make these words a part of his or her own vocabulary by using them when you talk together about matter and ways that it changes.

> physical change
> states of matter
> mixture
> solution
> chemical change

These following pages include activities that you and your child can do together. By participating in your child's education, you will help to bring the learning home.

Family Science Activity
The Cornstarch Experiment

Help your child learn about changes in matter by performing a simple experiment with cornstarch and water. This material is unusual because it can act both like a solid and a liquid. When you squeeze the wet cornstarch, it acts like a solid. When you do not touch it, it acts like a liquid.

Materials
- large mixing bowl
- 1 cup cornstarch
- about 1/2 cup water
- spoon
- pie plate

Steps

1. Place the cornstarch in the bowl.
2. Stir SLOWLY as you add a little water at a time until the cornstarch and water are about as thick as pancake batter. (Less water is better than too much water because you can always add more water if needed.)
3. Have your child put his or her hands in the cornstarch and water mixture. Record what happens.
4. Have your child try to roll a ball. Record what happens.
5. Pour water into the pie plate. Have your child slap it and record what happens.
6. Empty the water from the pie plate and pour some of the cornstarch and water into it. Have your child slap it and record what happens.

Workbook

Vocabulary Crossword

Complete the puzzle with the clues you will find on the next page.

Crossword Clues

Down

1. What you call pieces of rice and vegetables tossed together.

2. What you call liquid when it becomes gas and solid when it becomes liquid.

Across

3. The kind of change that happens when you pull apart sections of an orange.

4. What you have when you dissolve soap in water.

5. What happens to change cookie dough into cookies.

Word Bank

physical change
mixture
chemical change
states of change
solution

Name _____

Write the vocabulary word that answers each riddle.

position	motion	relative position
speed	force	gravity
friction	weight	work

1. It tells the location of something. It is specific. Every place on a map has this. What is it? _____

2. It is a force. It opposes motion. It slows moving objects. What is it? _____

3. It is a push or a pull. It can result from two objects coming in contact. It can also result when an object does not touch anything. What is it? _____

4. It locates one thing in relationship to other things. It changes when direction of motion changes. What is it?

   _____

5. It pulls objects toward each other. It is a force. It does not require contact. It increases as mass increases. What is it?

   _____

6. You have this because of gravity. On Earth, it is about the same as mass. It decreases as you travel away from the center of Earth. What is it? _____

7. This tells how fast something changes position. It is a rate of change. It can be fast or slow. It can be constant or variable. What is it? _____

8. You do this when you move something. Machines can help you do this more easily. What is it? _____

9. Anytime an object changes position, this is involved. When your bike rolls, this would be described as forward. When Earth rotates, this is described as circular. What is it?

   _____

Notes for Home: Your child learned the vocabulary terms for Chapter 12.
Home Activity: Ask your child to explain the vocabulary terms to you using photos, diagrams, and other graphics in the chapter to help.

Summarize

Read the science article.

Force

Some forces can cause objects to move without touching them. The force of gravity, for example, pulls a ball that you throw back to Earth. Gravity from the Moon and the Sun tugs at the oceans and causes high and low tides. A magnet also exerts a force. It can pull a metal object to itself from inches, or even feet, away.

Apply It!

Fill in the graphic organizer. Write three details and a summary of the article on page 110.

Notes for Home: Your child learned how to use details in a summary.
Home Activity: With your child, read an article about something in motion. Together decide what are the important details in the article and summarize them.

Notes

Lesson 1: What happens when things change position?

Before You Read Lesson 1

Read each statement below. Place a check mark in the circle to indicate whether you agree or disagree with the statement.

	Agree	Disagree
1. Motion is change of position.	○	○
2. An object with variable speed moves at the same rate.	○	○
3. A constant speed is always fast.	○	○

After You Read Lesson 1

Reread each statement above. If the lesson supports your choice, place a check mark in the *Correct* circle. Then explain how the text supports your choice. If the lesson does not support your choice, place a check mark in the *Incorrect* circle. Then explain why your choice is wrong.

	Correct	Incorrect
1. _____	○	○
_____		
2. _____	○	○
_____		
3. _____	○	○
_____		

Notes for Home: Your child has completed a pre/post inventory of key concepts in the lesson.
Home Activity: Have your child use toy cars or other movable objects to demonstrate slow, fast, constant, and variable speed.

Reviewing Terms: Sentence Completion

Complete each sentence with the correct word or phrase.

_____ 1. An object's _____ compares its position to the position of other objects. (relative position, speed)

_____ 2. An object that is in _____ keeps changing position. (relative position, motion)

_____ 3. An object's location is its _____. (position, speed)

_____ 4. _____ is how fast an object changes position. (Motion, Speed)

Reviewing Concepts: True or False

Write **T** (True) or **F** (False) on the line before each statement.

_____ 5. A map is a drawing of a place that shows the position of objects.

_____ 6. Words like *forward*, *left*, and *right* can describe the position of an object.

_____ 7. All objects move at the same speed.

_____ 8. A constant speed is a speed that is always changing.

Applying Strategies: Calculating

9. If a family biked 18 kilometers in 3 hours, what was their average speed in kilometers per hour? Show your work. (2 points)

Lesson 2: How does force affect motion?

Before You Read Lesson 2

Read each statement below. Place a check mark in the circle to indicate whether you agree or disagree with the statement.

	Agree	Disagree
1. Gravity causes you to have weight.	○	○
2. Friction always helps objects move faster.	○	○
3. Motion is often the result of many forces.	○	○

After You Read Lesson 2

Reread each statement above. If the lesson supports your choice, place a check mark in the *Correct* circle. Then explain how the text supports your choice. If the lesson does not support your choice, place a check mark in the *Incorrect* circle. Then explain why your choice is wrong.

	Correct	Incorrect
1. _____	○	○
_____		
2. _____	○	○
_____		
3. _____	○	○
_____		

Notes for Home: Your child has completed a pre/post inventory of key concepts in the lesson.
Home Activity: Have your child push a toy car or other wheeled object over a wood or tiled floor, then a carpeted floor. Talk about which surface produced more friction.

Reviewing Terms: Matching

Match each description with the correct word. Write the letter on the line next to each description.

_____ 1. any push or pull

_____ 2. a contact force that goes against motion

_____ 3. a non-contact force that pulls all objects together and all objects toward the center of Earth

_____ 4. a non-contact force that pulls on metals with iron in them

a. magnetism

b. force

c. gravity

d. friction

Reviewing Concepts: True or False

Write **T** (True) or **F** (False) on the line before each statement.

_____ 5. Forces can change an object's motion.

_____ 6. Friction can cause a moving object to slow down or to stop.

_____ 7. Equal forces in opposite directions change an object's motion.

_____ 8. Weight is the amount of gravity that pulls on an object.

Applying Strategies: Summarize

Use a complete sentence to answer question 9. (2 points)

9. Write a sentence that summarizes how forces affect motion.

_____

_____

_____

Name _____

Lesson 3: How do simple machines affect work?

Before You Read Lesson 3

Read each statement below. Place a check mark in the circle to indicate whether you agree or disagree with the statement.

	Agree	Disagree
1. Pushing on a mountain is work.	○	○
2. A wedge is used to split or cut.	○	○
3. A lever rests on a support.	○	○

After You Read Lesson 3

Reread each statement above. If the lesson supports your choice, place a check mark in the *Correct* circle. Then explain how the text supports your choice. If the lesson does not support your choice, place a check mark in the *Incorrect* circle. Then explain why your choice is wrong.

	Correct	Incorrect
1. _____	○	○
_____		
2. _____	○	○
_____		
3. _____	○	○
_____		

Notes for Home: Your child has completed a pre/post inventory of key concepts in the lesson.
Home Activity: Help your child identify an example of each simple machine among his or her toys or among household objects.

Reviewing Terms: Sentence Completion

Complete the sentence with the correct word.

_____ 1. _____ is done when a force moves an object. (Work, Distance)

Reviewing Concepts: Sentence Completion

Complete each sentence with the correct word or phrase.

_____ 2. Machines _____ change the amount of work needed to do a task. (do, do not)

_____ 3. A ramp is an example of a(n) _____. (pulley, inclined plane)

_____ 4. One example of a _____ is a knife. (wedge, screw)

_____ 5. An inclined plane wrapped around a center post is a _____. (screw, wedge)

_____ 6. A seesaw is one kind of _____. (pulley, lever)

_____ 7. A doorknob is a(n) _____ that makes opening a door easier. (wheel and axle, inclined plane)

_____ 8. You can use a _____ to change the direction of your force. (pulley, wedge)

Writing

Use complete sentences to answer question 9. (2 points)

9. Write a paragraph that tells about a time when you used a simple machine to make work easier.

_____

_____

_____

Relating Speed, Distance, and Time

Use the formulas to solve the word problems.

$$\text{Distance} = \text{Time} \times \text{Speed}$$

$$\text{Time} = \frac{\text{Distance}}{\text{Speed}}$$

$$\text{Speed} = \frac{\text{Distance}}{\text{Time}}$$

To:
Lake Quahanon   4 km
Feather Falls   8 km
General Store   10 km

1. Dennis and Anita rode their bikes an average speed of 8 km per hour. How long did it take them to get to Feather Falls? _____

2. They rode to the General Store and back. It took them 2 hours. How fast did they ride? _____

3. If Dennis and Anita ride to all three places and back, one at a time, and it takes them 4 hours, what was their average speed? _____

Notes for Home: Your child learned to calculate speed, distance, and time.
Home Activity: Walk, drive, or ride with your child to a location whose distance you know. Measure the time it takes. Then calculate your average speed.

Notes

Dear Family,

Your child is learning about forces and motion. In the science chapter Forces and Motion, our class has learned different ways to describe position and motion. We also investigated how forces affect the motion of objects. Students also learned about simple machines and how they help us do work more easily.

Students also learned many new vocabulary words. Help your child to make these words a part of his or her own vocabulary by using them when you talk together about force, motion, and work.

position
motion
relative position
speed
force
friction
gravity
magnetism
work

The following pages include activities that you and your child can do together. By participating in your child's education, you will help to bring the learning home.

Family Science Activity
Slide for Speed

Help your child observe force and motion by noting the speed of different objects as they move down a slide.

Materials:
- Slide
- 2 balls; one ball should be noticeably heavier
- Paper and pencil

Steps

1 Before you go outside, help your child choose two balls. Have your child compare the balls is terms of their size and weight.

2 Go to a park or playground with a slide. Have your child go to the top of the slide and hold each ball, side by side.

3 Direct your child to release both balls. Which one moves faster? Why? Have your child record the results. Repeat the experiment.

4 Have your child draw a picture of your experiment. Have him or her write a few sentences that tell what happened.

Workbook

Vocabulary Practice

Read the story and underline the vocabulary words wherever they appear.

José said, "Watch me work. My body will be a force that makes this rock move with speed down the hill."

"You can change the position of the rock with your body?" Anna asked.

"Of course," José boasted.

Anna added, "Gravity can also pull a rock down a hill." Anna pulled a magnet out of her backpack. "Magnetism can change the position of a rock, too." Anna placed the magnet by a rock. It turned to the right.

"Wow!" José exclaimed.

Anna smiled and said, "Now, let's see you move that big, big rock all by yourself."

Finding Work

Work is when you use force to move an object. **Look** at the pictures below. **Circle** the pictures that show work being done.

1.

2.

3.

4.

Name _____

Write the words in the blanks.

potential energy	kinetic energy	thermal energy
reflect	refract	absorb
electric charge	electric current	electric circuit

A. Kinds of Energy

| _____ (stored) | _____ (moving objects) | _____ (produces heat) | Chemical energy | Electrical energy | Light energy |

B. Light Energy—It moves in a straight line until it hits an object.

Light can _____ or bounce.

It can _____ or bend.

It can be _____ or soak in.

C. Electricity

Particles of matter have an _____ _____.

An _____ _____ causes the bulb to light.

Electricity flows through an _____.

Notes for Home: Your child learned the vocabulary terms for Chapter 13.
Home Activity: Ask your child to explain the vocabulary terms to you, using the diagrams and illustrations in their text.

© Pearson Education, Inc.

◎ Main Idea and Supporting Details

Read the science article.

Energy in Motion

Energy is always in motion. Look around you and you will see many examples. A bike racing downhill carries energy. Energy moves through wires as electric current. Heat energy moves from a warm object to a cooler object.

Apply It!

Write the main idea of the science article in the box on the next page. Then write details that support the main idea in the circles.

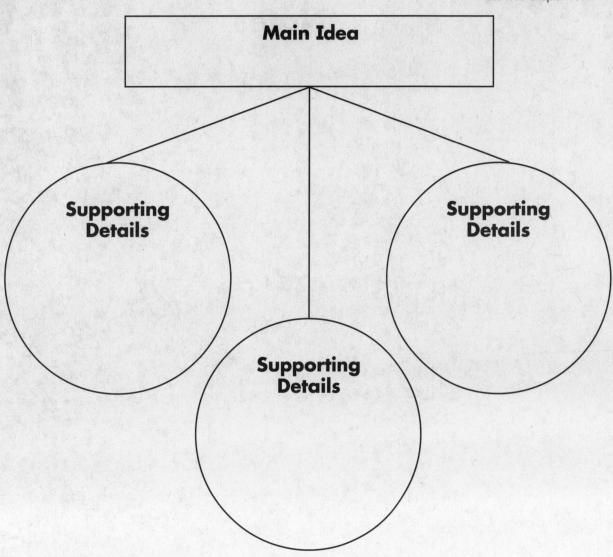

Main Idea

Supporting Details

Supporting Details

Supporting Details

Notes for Home: Your child learned how to identify main ideas and supporting details.

Home Activity: With your child, find and read an article in a magazine. Ask your child to find the main idea of a paragraph in the article and point out supporting details.

Notes

Lesson 1: What is energy?

Before You Read Lesson 1

Read each statement below. Place a check mark in the circle to indicate whether you agree or disagree with the statement.

	Agree	Disagree
1. The Sun gives us heat and light energy.	○	○
2. A pile of coal has potential energy.	○	○
3. A car in the garage has kinetic energy.	○	○

After You Read Lesson 1

Reread each statement above. If the lesson supports your choice, place a check mark in the *Correct* circle. Then explain how the text supports your choice. If the lesson does not support your choice, place a check mark in the *Incorrect* circle. Then explain why your choice is wrong.

	Correct	Incorrect
1. _____ _____	○	○
2. _____ _____	○	○
3. _____ _____	○	○

Notes for Home: Your child has completed a pre/post inventory of key concepts in the lesson.
Home Activity: Have your child help you make a snack. Talk about the forms of potential and kinetic energy involved in the task. Discuss how your body uses the energy.

Reviewing Terms: Matching

Match each description with the correct phrase. Write the letter on the line next to each description.

_____ 1. stored energy

_____ 2. energy of motion

a. potential energy

b. kinetic energy

Reviewing Concepts: True or False

Write **T** (True) or **F** (False) on the line before each statement.

_____ 3. Energy can change form.

_____ 4. Energy is the ability to do work or to cause change.

_____ 5. There is one form of energy.

_____ 6. Fuels store kinetic energy.

_____ 7. Chemical energy can be stored in batteries.

_____ 8. Potential energy can change to kinetic energy.

Writing

Use complete sentences to answer question 9. (2 points)

9. Describe one example of potential energy and one example of kinetic energy with which you are familiar.

_____

_____

_____

_____

© Pearson Education, Inc.

Lesson 2: How does energy change form?

Before You Read Lesson 2

Read each statement below. Place a check mark in the circle to indicate whether you agree or disagree with the statement.

	Agree	Disagree
1. A carrot holds chemical energy.	○	○
2. Electrical charges give off heat.	○	○
3. Energy is often useful when it is changing form.	○	○

After You Read Lesson 2

Reread each statement above. If the lesson supports your choice, place a check mark in the *Correct* circle. Then explain how the text supports your choice. If the lesson does not support your choice, place a check mark in the *Incorrect* circle. Then explain why your choice is wrong.

	Correct	Incorrect
1. _____	○	○
_____		
2. _____	○	○
_____		
3. _____	○	○
_____		

 Notes for Home: Your child has completed a pre/post inventory of key concepts in the lesson.
Home Activity: With your child, make waves using a spiral wire toy. Identify the trough and crest. Note how the waves change as you add more energy with your arms.

Reviewing Concepts: Sentence Completion

Complete each sentence with the correct word.

_____ 1. Your body uses the _____ energy in food. (electrical, chemical)

_____ 2. When energy changes form, some energy is always given off as _____. (heat, light)

_____ 3. The energy in moving objects is _____ energy. (thermal, mechanical)

_____ 4. The appliances in people's homes are powered by _____ energy. (electrical, light)

_____ 5. Plants use _____ energy from the Sun to make food. (chemical, light)

_____ 6. Waves carry _____. (water, energy)

_____ 7. As waves move away from their source, they _____ energy. (gain, lose)

_____ 8. Waves that are _____ have lots of energy. (wide, narrow)

Writing

Use complete sentences to answer question 9. (2 points)

9. Write a paragraph that describes energy changing from one form to another.

_____

_____

_____

_____

Lesson 3: What is heat energy?

Before You Read Lesson 3

Read each statement below. Place a check mark in the circle to indicate whether you agree or disagree with the statement.

	Agree	Disagree
1. Thermal energy comes from the motion of particles.	○	○
2. Heat travels from cooler to warmer matter.	○	○
3. Heat can change the state of matter.	○	○

After You Read Lesson 3

Reread each statement above. If the lesson supports your choice, place a check mark in the *Correct* circle. Then explain how the text supports your choice. If the lesson does not support your choice, place a check mark in the *Incorrect* circle. Then explain why your choice is wrong.

	Correct	Incorrect
1. _____ _____	○	○
2. _____ _____	○	○
3. _____ _____	○	○

Notes for Home: Your child has completed a pre/post inventory of key concepts in the lesson.
Home Activity: With your child, make juice pops in an ice tray. Discuss why heat moved from the liquid juice into the freezer and what changed because of the loss.

Reviewing Terms: Sentence Completion

Complete the sentence with the correct phrase.

_____ 1. The energy of moving particles is _____.
(thermal energy, electrical energy)

Reviewing Concepts: True or False

Write **T** (True) or **F** (False) on the line before each statement.

_____ 2. Thermal energy travels as heat.

_____ 3. Heat moves from cooler objects to warmer objects.

_____ 4. When energy changes form, some heat is given off.

_____ 5. The change from ice to liquid water is related to a change in energy.

_____ 6. Friction caused by rubbing gives off heat.

_____ 7. Heat can cause water to evaporate.

_____ 8. Liquid water boils as it turns to ice.

Applying Strategies: Calculating

9. On the Fahrenheit scale, water boils at 212 degrees and freezes at 32 degrees. What is the difference between these two temperatures? Show your work. (2 points)

Lesson 4: What is light energy?

Before You Read Lesson 4

Read each statement below. Place a check mark in the circle to indicate whether you agree or disagree with the statement.

	Agree	Disagree
1. Only the Sun and chemical changes produce light.	○	○
2. Reflected light bounces off a smooth surface.	○	○
3. Color results from refracted light.	○	○

After You Read Lesson 4

Reread each statement above. If the lesson supports your choice, place a check mark in the *Correct* circle. Then explain how the text supports your choice. If the lesson does not support your choice, place a check mark in the *Incorrect* circle. Then explain why your choice is wrong.

	Correct	Incorrect
1. _____	○	○
_____		
2. _____	○	○
_____		
3. _____	○	○
_____		

Notes for Home: Your child has completed a pre/post inventory of key concepts in the lesson.
Home Activity: With your child, place a black cloth and a white cloth in sunlight. Discuss why the black cloth absorbs more heat than the white cloth.

Reviewing Terms: Matching

Match each description with the correct word or phrase. Write the letter on the line next to each description.

_____ 1. light bouncing off an object

_____ 2. light bending

_____ 3. light being taken in by an object

a. absorb

b. reflect

c. refract

Reviewing Concepts: Sentence Completion

Complete each sentence with the correct word or phrase.

_____ 4. _____ is energy that can be seen. (Light, Heat)

_____ 5. Light bulbs use _____ to make light. (electrical energy, chemical energy)

_____ 6. Light travels from its source in _____. (straight lines, curved lines)

_____ 7. The length of a shadow depends on the _____ of the light. (brightness, angle)

_____ 8. Light is made up of _____ colors. (one, many)

Applying Strategies: Main Idea and Supporting Details

Use complete sentences to answer question 9. (2 points)

9. List three details that support the main idea below.

Main Idea: Objects can reflect, refract, or absorb light.

Detail: _____

Detail: _____

Detail: _____

_____

© Pearson Education, Inc.

Lesson 5: What is electrical energy?

Before You Read Lesson 5

Read each statement below. Place a check mark in the circle to indicate whether you agree or disagree with the statement.

	Agree	Disagree
1. Lightning is a kind of electric circuit.	○	○
2. Electric energy can be changed to sound energy.	○	○
3. An open switch breaks an electric circuit.	○	○

After You Read Lesson 5

Reread each statement above. If the lesson supports your choice, place a check mark in the *Correct* circle. Then explain how the text supports your choice. If the lesson does not support your choice, place a check mark in the *Incorrect* circle. Then explain why your choice is wrong.

	Correct	Incorrect
1. _____ _____	○	○
2. _____ _____	○	○
3. _____ _____	○	○

Notes for Home: Your child has completed a pre/post inventory of key concepts in the lesson.
Home Activity: With your child, list appliances in your home that use electricity. Make a chart to sort the appliances into those used to produce light, heat, and sound.

Reviewing Terms: Matching

Match each description with the correct phrase. Write the letter on the line next to each description.

_____ 1. a tiny amount of energy, this can be positive or negative

_____ 2. movement of electrical energy or electrical charge

_____ 3. the path through which an electric current flows

a. electric circuit
b. electric charge
c. electric current

Reviewing Concepts: True or False

Write **T** (True) or **F** (False) on the line before each statement.

_____ 4. Particles balance each other when they have an equal number of positive and negative charges.

_____ 5. Two objects with negative charges will attract each other.

_____ 6. Lightning is an uncontrolled electric current.

_____ 7. When the switch in an electric circuit is open, current can flow.

_____ 8. Electrical energy is changed to sound energy in a radio speaker.

Applying Strategies: Compare and Contrast

Use complete sentences to answer question 9. (2 points)

9. Describe one similarity and one difference between the electricity in lightning and the electricity in an electrical circuit.

_____

_____

_____

_____

Measuring Temperature

Mickie used the thermometer below to measure the temperatures of tap water and bath water.

Use the thermometer to answer the questions. Place a ruler to help you compare degrees Celsius and degrees Fahrenheit.

1. Mickie found that her bath water was 120°F. About how many degrees Celsius is this? _____

2. The water from the tap was about 18°C. Which of the following is closest to this temperature in degrees Fahrenheit?

   A. 30°F   **B.** 45°F   **C.** 60°F   **D.** 75°F

   _____

3. Mickie took her temperature. It was 37°C. Normal body temperature in degrees Fahrenheit is 98.6. Did Mickie have a fever? How do you know? _____

   _____

Notes for Home: Your child measured temperature in degrees Fahrenheit and Celsius.
Home Activity: Help your child measure his or her temperature in degrees Fahrenheit and convert this to degrees Celsius. (Use the formula $F = (C \times 9/5) + 32$ to check the estimate.)

Notes

Dear Family,

Your child is learning about the many forms of energy we use every day, from the chemical energy stored in food and fuel to the kinetic energy of a moving object. In the chapter Energy, we also explored electrical energy, light energy, and thermal energy. Your child studied how energy can change forms. For example, a hair dryer turns electricity into heat, sound, and kinetic energy.

Your child learned many new vocabulary words in this chapter. Help your child to make these words a part of his or her own vocabulary by using them when you talk together about energy.

potential energy
kinetic energy
thermal energy
reflect
refract
absorb
electric charge
electric current
electric circuit

The following pages include activities that you and your child can do together. By participating in your child's education, you will help to bring the learning home.

Family Science Activity
Energy Watch

Use this chart to keep a family energy survey. Write an example of the five forms of energy you use every day. Energy is a part of every movement we make, so you won't be able to include every example. Choose interesting examples and talk about how this energy was useful in your activities.

Chemical	Kinetic	Electrical	Light	Thermal

Talk About It

Which form of energy do you think you use the most every day? Why? What would your life be like without electricity? Make a list of your habits and hobbies that would have to change.

Vocabulary Practice: Energy

Write a vocabulary word to answer each clue. The shaded letters will spell the answer to the question on the next page. You can see a list of the vocabulary words on page 1 of the booklet.

1.
2.
3.
4.
5.
6.
7.
8.
9.

1. An electric _____ must be unbroken for energy to flow through it.
2. Electric _____ is the movement of electrical energy from one place to another.
3. A mirror will _____ light when it bounces the light back to your eyes.
4. The energy of motion is _____ energy.
5. An electric _____ is a tiny amount of energy.
6. If an object looks black, it will _____ all the colors of sunlight.
7. Light rays bend when they _____.
8. Stored energy is _____ energy.
9. The energy of moving particles is _____ energy.

What invention by Samuel Morse sends messages by making and breaking an electric circuit?

Fun Fact

Calories measure the energy stored in food. When you look at the calorie content of any food, you are looking at how much energy the food could give your body.

ANSWERS: 1. circuit; 2. current; 3. reflect; 4. kinetic; 5. charge; 6. absorb; 7. refract; 8. potential; 9. thermal

Workbook

Name _____

Write a vocabulary term from the word bank to complete each sentence. Underline the clues that helped you decide which vocabulary term to write.

pitch	**vibration**	**compression wave**

1. Energy causes particles of matter to move back and forth. It is this _____ that produces sound.

2. Wave motion involves passing energy through particles. Some particles are squeezed together while others are spread apart. This is called a _____.

3. A bass string vibrates slowly and produces a low sound. A violin string vibrates quickly and produces a high sound. This is a difference in _____.

Explain what is happening in the picture. Write three sentences. Use a vocabulary word in each sentence.

4. _____

5. _____

6. _____

 Notes for Home: Your child learned the vocabulary terms for Chapter 14.
Home Activity: Ask your child to demonstrate or illustrate the meaning of each vocabulary term as he or she explains it to you.

Use with Chapter 14.

 # Compare and Contrast

Read the paragraph.

Musical Instruments

A trombone and a bassoon are both wind instruments. This means they make sounds when you cause the air in them to vibrate. A trombonist vibrates his or her lips and blows into the trombone mouthpiece. This makes the air inside the instrument vibrate. A bassoonist blows on a reed, or a thin piece of wood. This makes the air in the bassoon vibrate.

Apply It!

Fill in the graphic organizer. Write ways the trombone and the bassoon are alike and ways they are different.

Trombone
Different

Both
Alike

Bassoon
Different

Notes for Home: Your child learned how to compare and contrast objects.
Home Activity: With your child, listen to a recording of music. Identify several instruments. Discuss how their sounds are different and how they might be produced.

Notes

Lesson 1: What causes sounds?

Before You Read Lesson 1

Read each statement below. Place a check mark in the circle to indicate whether you agree or disagree with the statement.

	Agree	Disagree
1. When you speak, your vocal chords vibrate.	○	○
2. Pitch is loudness or softness of sound.	○	○
3. Short, thin harp strings make high sounds.	○	○

After You Read Lesson 1

Reread each statement above. If the lesson supports your choice, place a check mark in the *Correct* circle. Then explain how the text supports your choice. If the lesson does not support your choice, place a check mark in the *Incorrect* circle. Then explain why your choice is wrong.

	Correct	Incorrect
1. _____ _____	○	○
2. _____ _____	○	○
3. _____ _____	○	○

Notes for Home: Your child has completed a pre/post inventory of key concepts in the lesson.
Home Activity: Have your child experiment with pitch and loudness by strumming stretched rubber bands with a finger and tapping glasses with a spoon.

Reviewing Terms: Matching

Match each description with the correct word or phrase. Write the letter on the line next to each description.

_____ 1. a back-and-forth motion

_____ 2. how high or low a sound is

a. pitch

b. vibration

Reviewing Concepts: Sentence Completion

Complete each sentence with the correct word.

_____ 3. _____ only happens when matter vibrates. (Sound, Light)

_____ 4. Objects that vibrate slowly make a sound with a _____ pitch. (high, low)

_____ 5. The _____ of sound depends on the strength of the vibrations. (pitch, loudness)

_____ 6. The harder you hit a drum, the _____ the sound. (louder, higher)

_____ 7. Wind instruments make sounds when _____ inside them vibrates. (string, air)

_____ 8. When people _____, their vocal chords vibrate. (speak, hear)

Applying Strategies: Compare and Contrast

Use complete sentences to answer question 9. (2 points)

9. Name one similarity and one difference between *pitch* and *loudness*.

_____

_____

_____

© Pearson Education, Inc.

Lesson 2: How does sound travel?

Before You Read Lesson 2

Read each statement below. Place a check mark in the circle to indicate whether you agree or disagree with the statement.

	Agree	Disagree
1. Without matter there is no sound.	○	○
2. Sound travels in compression waves.	○	○
3. Sound cannot travel through gases.	○	○

After You Read Lesson 2

Reread each statement above. If the lesson supports your choice, place a check mark in the *Correct* circle. Then explain how the text supports your choice. If the lesson does not support your choice, place a check mark in the *Incorrect* circle. Then explain why your choice is wrong.

	Correct	Incorrect
1. _____	○	○
_____		
2. _____	○	○
_____		
3. _____	○	○
_____		

Notes for Home: Your child has completed a pre/post inventory of key concepts in the lesson.
Home Activity: Have your child listen to a sound traveling through air, then through water, for example, in a bathtub.

Name _____

Reviewing Terms: Sentence Completion

Complete the sentence with the correct word.

_____ 1. Sound waves are examples of
_____ waves. (compression, atmospheric)

Reviewing Concepts: True or False

Write **T** (True) or **F** (False) on the line before each statement.

_____ 2. Sound travels in matter.

_____ 3. Sound cannot travel in outer space.

_____ 4. Sound travels through solids, but not through liquids and gases.

_____ 5. Echoes are caused when sound waves are absorbed by an object.

_____ 6. The outer ear collects sound waves traveling in the air.

_____ 7. Humans and animals can all hear the same sounds.

_____ 8. Bats use sound to find food.

Applying Strategies: Converting Units

9. The speed of sound in steel is 5,200 meters per second. Write this speed using the unit kilometers per second. Remember that 1,000 meters = 1 kilometer. Show your work. (2 points)

Comparing Speeds of Sound

Compare the speeds at which sound travels through the materials in the table. Use the data to answer the questions.

Materials	Speed (Meters Per Second)
Rubber	60
Cork	500
Lead	1,210
Water at 25° Celsius	1,496
Sea water at 25° Celsius	1,531
Brick	3,650
Glass	4,540
Aluminum	5,000
Stone	5,971

1. What solids carry sound slower than water carries it?

   _____

2. Does sound travel faster through fresh water or

   salt water? _____

3. Suppose an earthquake occurs in the ocean floor. What different materials will its sound travel through? How fast

   will it travel through each material? _____

   _____

   _____

Notes for Home: Your child compared the speeds at which sound travels through different materials.
Home Activity: Discuss with your child how the particles of the different materials in the chart might differ and how these differences affect their ability to transmit sound waves.

Notes

Dear Family,

Your child is learning how different sounds are produced. In the science chapter Sound, our class learned how sound travels. Students studied how humans produce sounds and how they hear. Our class also learned how certain musical instruments produce sounds.

In addition to learning how sound travels through different materials, students learned many new vocabulary words. Help your child to make these words a part of his or her own vocabulary by using them when you talk together about sound.

> vibration
> pitch
> compression wave

The following pages include activities that you and your child can do together. By participating in your child's education, you will help to bring the learning home.

© Pearson Education, Inc.

Family Science Activity
Sound Mysteries

Materials:

- piles of items, such as popcorn kernels, pennies, grains of rice, paper clips, pebbles, soil, or sand (NOTE: The piles should be similar in size.)
- four opaque plastic cups
- aluminum paper squares
- paper or pencil

Steps

1. Show your child each pile of items. Then, have your child leave the room while you place each item into a plastic cup. Place a foil square over each cups opening.

2. Invite your child to return to the room. Remove one cup's cover; place your hand over the top of the cup. Make sure your child cannot see what is inside the cup.

3. Shake the cup. Ask your child which of the four objects he or she heard rattle inside the cup. Have your child write Cup 1 and the name of the object on a piece of paper.

4. Return the cup to the table and cover it. Repeat Step 3 with Cups 2, 3, and 4.

5. Remove each cup's cover. Compare your child's guesses to the actual content in each cup.

Workbook

Vocabulary Practice

Find a vocabulary word in each list of letters.
Circle the letters of the word. Write the word
on the line.

Word Bank

vibration	pitch	compression wave

d h a p i w z y d x w t c h d i f t u x d

p c o m e i p r e s s r i o n t n w a v e x

s a d f q v i o b r a w l t i o n f w z b h d q

Answer with an Antonym

Antonyms are words that have the opposite
meaning of another word. Draw a line
from a word about sound on the left to its
antonym on the right.

1. to vibrate   silence

2. high   low

3. sound   soft

4. loud   to be still

5. receive   send

Fun Fact

Did you ever see a dog prick up its ears
and turn them toward a sound? Dogs move
their ears in order to hear well. A dog uses
more than eighteen different muscles to tilt,
raise, or turn its ears.

Name _____

Read each sentence. Choose the answer that gives the best meaning for the boldface word.

1. Earth makes a complete **rotation** every twenty-four hours.
   A. circle   B. spin   C. day   D. week

2. The Sun is a **star** that gives Earth heat and light.
   A. super-sized planet   C. very distant object
   B. huge rock   D. hot ball of gases

3. A full Moon and a crescent Moon are two Moon **phases**.
   A. stages   C. craters
   B. separate parts   D. copies

4. Earth spins on its **axis** like a wheel spins on an axle.
   A. east-to-west line   C. line from pole to pole
   B. flat pancake shape   D. force field that pulls

5. In a year, Earth makes one **revolution** around the Sun.
   A. circle around a center   C. set of seasons
   B. trip to and from   D. change of direction

6. In a **lunar eclipse**, Earth moves between the Sun and Moon.
   A. blocking of the Sun's light
   B. Earth's shadow covering Moon
   C. blocking of the Moon by Earth
   D. Moon's shadow covering Earth

7. A **telescope** shows details of the Moon and stars.
   A. tool that magnifies   C. lighted tube
   B. tool that makes   D. darkened pipe
      things look smaller

8. Long ago, people named each **constellation** of stars.
   A. any cluster of stars   C. group of stars in a pattern
   B. quarter of the sky   D. half of the sky

Notes for Home: Your child learned the vocabulary terms for Chapter 15.
Home Activity: Ask your child to find an example or diagram in the chapter to help explain the meaning of each vocabulary word.

⊙ Sequence

Study the set of diagrams that show a pattern.

Apply It!

In the box below, draw a diagram of what will happen next in the pattern. Show the shadow that will appear and its direction.

© Pearson Education, Inc.

Notes for Home: Your child learned how to use a diagrammed sequence to predict what will happen next.
Home Activity: With your child, use a flashlight and an object to make shadows. Describe the sequence of movements that makes the shadow lengthen.

Notes

Lesson 1: What are some patterns that repeat every day?

Before You Read Lesson 1

Read each statement below. Place a check mark in the circle to indicate whether you agree or disagree with the statement.

	Agree	Disagree
1. Earth's rotation causes day and night.	○	○
2. Earth rotates faster in winter.	○	○
3. Shadows fall to the east in the morning.	○	○

After You Read Lesson 1

Reread each statement above. If the lesson supports your choice, place a check mark in the *Correct* circle. Then explain how the text supports your choice. If the lesson does not support your choice, place a check mark in the *Incorrect* circle. Then explain why your choice is wrong.

	Correct	Incorrect
1. _____	○	○
_____		
2. _____	○	○
_____		
3. _____	○	○
_____		

Notes for Home: Your child has completed a pre/post inventory of key concepts in the lesson.
Home Activity: Have your child use a ball or globe to model Earth's rotation while you hold a flashlight. Discuss how rotation causes day and night.

Reviewing Terms: Matching

Match each description with the correct word. Write the letter on the line next to each description.

_____ 1. a giant ball of hot, glowing gases   **a.** axis

_____ 2. the imaginary line around which   **b.** star
          Earth spins   **c.** rotation

_____ 3. one complete spin on an axis

Reviewing Concepts: Sentence Completion

Complete each sentence with the correct word or phrase.

_____ 4. Earth is _____ compared to the Sun. (large, small)

_____ 5. At any time, _____ of Earth is facing the Sun. (half, all)

_____ 6. Earth makes one rotation every _____ hours. (12, 24)

_____ 7. The length and direction of shadows _____ throughout the day. (change, stay the same)

_____ 8. Shadows are very _____ at midday. (long, short)

Applying Strategies: Sequence

9. The Sun's place in the sky seems to change throughout the day. The steps are listed below, but they are out of order. Use the clue words to place the steps in the correct order. (2 points)

Finally, the Sun appears to set in the west.
First, the Sun appears to rise in the east.
Next, the Sun appears to move across the sky.

_____

_____

_____

Lesson 2: What patterns repeat every year?

Before You Read Lesson 2

Read each statement below. Place a check mark in the circle to indicate whether you agree or disagree with the statement.

	Agree	Disagree
1. A revolution is one complete spin.	○	○
2. December is summer time in the southern half of Earth.	○	○
3. We have less sunlight in winter.	○	○

After You Read Lesson 2

Reread each statement above. If the lesson supports your choice, place a check mark in the *Correct* circle. Then explain how the text supports your choice. If the lesson does not support your choice, place a check mark in the *Incorrect* circle. Then explain why your choice is wrong.

	Correct	Incorrect
1. _____ _____	○	○
2. _____ _____	○	○
3. _____ _____	○	○

 Notes for Home: Your child has completed a pre/post inventory of key concepts in the lesson.
Home Activity: With your child, use a flashlight and a ball held at a tilted angle to model direct and indirect rays of light hitting a sphere.

Reviewing Terms: Sentence Completion

Complete the sentence with the correct word.

_____ 1. A _____ is one complete trip around the Sun.
(revolution, rotation)

Reviewing Concepts: True or False

Write **T** (True) or **F** (False) on the line before each statement.

_____ 2. Earth's axis always points toward the same direction in space.

_____ 3. The places on Earth that receive the most direct Sun are the warmest.

_____ 4. The seasons are caused by Earth's tilt and movement around the Sun.

_____ 5. Earth makes one revolution in 24 hours.

_____ 6. In most places on Earth the number of hours of daylight and darkness changes throughout the year.

_____ 7. During winter there are more hours of daylight than darkness.

_____ 8. The Sun appears higher in the sky during summer than it does in winter.

Applying Strategies: Calculating

9. In the Northern United States there are 15 hours of daylight on some days during June. On those days, how many hours of darkness are there? Show your work, and write a sentence that explains how you found your answer. (2 points)

_____

_____

_____

Lesson 3: Why does the Moon's shape change?

Before You Read Lesson 3

Read each statement below. Place a check mark in the circle to indicate whether you agree or disagree with the statement.

	Agree	**Disagree**
1. The Moon reflects sunlight.	○	○
2. The Moon changes shape each month.	○	○
3. The Moon repeats four phases each $29\frac{1}{2}$ days.	○	○

After You Read Lesson 3

Reread each statement above. If the lesson supports your choice, place a check mark in the *Correct* circle. Then explain how the text supports your choice. If the lesson does not support your choice, place a check mark in the *Incorrect* circle. Then explain why your choice is wrong.

	Correct	**Incorrect**
1. _____ _____	○	○
2. _____ _____	○	○
3. _____ _____	○	○

Notes for Home: Your child has completed a pre/post inventory of key concepts in the lesson.
Home Activity: With your child, observe the Moon, draw it, and identify its phase. Observe and sketch it again several days later and compare how it looks.

Reviewing Terms: Matching

Match each description with the correct word or phrase. Write the letter on the line next to each description.

_____ 1. each different way the Moon looks
_____ 2. when Earth blocks sunlight from reaching the Moon

a. lunar eclipse
b. phase

Reviewing Concepts: True or False

Write **T** (True) or **F** (False) on the line before each statement.

_____ 3. It takes the Moon about 29 days to complete one rotation.

_____ 4. The Moon makes its own light.

_____ 5. During a New Moon, the Moon looks like a half circle.

_____ 6. The Moon looks like a half circle during the First Quarter Moon.

_____ 7. The Full Moon looks like a circle.

_____ 8. The lighted half of the Moon can always be seen from Earth.

Writing

9. Write a paragraph that describes the positions of the Earth, Moon, and Sun during a lunar eclipse. (2 points)

_____

_____

_____

_____

Name _____

Lesson 4: What are star patterns?

Before You Read Lesson 4

Read each statement below. Place a check mark in the circle to indicate whether you agree or disagree with the statement.

	Agree	Disagree
1. Stars in a constellation make a pattern.	○	○
2. Most stars can be seen with the eyes alone.	○	○
3. Stars are moving in space.	○	○

After You Read Lesson 4

Reread each statement above. If the lesson supports your choice, place a check mark in the *Correct* circle. Then explain how the text supports your choice. If the lesson does not support your choice, place a check mark in the *Incorrect* circle. Then explain why your choice is wrong.

	Correct	Incorrect
1. _____	○	○
_____		
2. _____	○	○
_____		
3. _____	○	○
_____		

Notes for Home: Your child has completed a pre/post inventory of key concepts in the lesson.
Home Activity: With your child, locate an outdoor space to view stars at night. (If possible, find a location that is not brightly lit.) Look for a constellation.

© Pearson Education, Inc.

Name _____

Reviewing Terms: Matching
Match each description with the correct word. Write the letter on the line next to each description.

_____ 1. a group of stars that makes a pattern

_____ 2. a tool that magnifies faraway objects

a. telescope

b. constellation

Reviewing Concepts: True or False
Write **T** (True) or **F** (False) on the line before each statement.

_____ 3. All stars are the same size.

_____ 4. Some stars are brighter than others.

_____ 5. Some telescopes use mirrors and lenses.

_____ 6. The stars in constellations are close together in space.

_____ 7. Stars appear to move across the sky at night.

_____ 8. Constellations always appear in the same part of the sky.

Applying Strategies: Main Idea and Supporting Details
Use complete sentences to answer question 9. (2 points)

9. Write three details that support the main idea given below.
Main Idea: Stars appear in patterns in the sky.

Detail: _____

Detail: _____

Detail: _____

Name _____

Comparing Times of Moonrise and Moonset

Like the Sun, the Moon rises and sets every day. However, the time of moonrise and moonset varies more than sunrise and sunset do. Use the table below to answer the questions.

DATE	MOONRISE	MOONSET
May 9, 2004	1:00 A.M.	9:48 A.M.
July 9, 2004	12:28 A.M.	1:34 P.M.
September 9, 2004	12:55 A.M.	5:04 P.M.
November 9, 2004	2:59 A.M.	3:09 P.M.

1. How many hours and minutes were between moonrise and moonset on May 9?

   _____

2. Which date had the longest time between moonrise and moonset?

   _____

3. If you stayed up to see the Moon rise, on which date would you stay up the longest?

   _____

4. Put the dates in order, from shortest time to longest time between moonrise and moonset.

   _____

Notes for Home: Your child used a table to calculate elapsed time.
Home Activity: Study the table with your child. Decide if the Moon can only be found in the sky at night or both at night and during daylight hours.

Notes

Dear Family,

Your child is learning about the different ways Earth and the Moon move. In the science chapter Patterns in the Sky, our class learned about Earth's rotation and its revolution around the Sun. Students also learned why the Moon appears to change shape throughout the month.

In addition to learning about Earth's movement and how it affects the seasons, students have also learned many new vocabulary words. Help your child to make these words a part of his or her own vocabulary by using them when you talk together about Earth's cycles.

star
axis
rotation
revolution
phase
lunar eclipse
telescope
constellation

The following pages include activities that you and your child can do together. By participating in your child's education, you will help to bring the learning home.

© Pearson Education, Inc.

Family Science Activity
Sunrise/Sunset Patterns

Materials:

- paper
- pen or pencil
- newspaper (optional)

Steps

1. Choose to record the time the Sun rises in the morning, or the time the Sun sets in the evening, or both. This depends on the season and your schedule.

2. Help your child make a chart. Divide the chart into two columns. Entitle one column *Date*, the other column *Time*.

3. Every day for the next couple of weeks, invite your child to go outside and watch the Sun rise or set. He or she should record the date and time when the first or last rays of the Sun are visible. (You may wish to compare these times with official sunrise and sunset times on the weather page of the newspaper.)

4. After two weeks, look at the chart. Ask your child to explain the pattern he or she has recorded. Are the daylight hours getting longer or shorter? Why? How will the number of daylight hours change during the next season?

Workbook

Phases of the Moon

Look at the pictures of the Moon below.
Draw lines to match the pictures on the left with the phase of the Moon on the right.

New Moon

Full Moon

First Quarter

Crescent

Your Favorite Season

Draw the weather for your favorite season.

Write about your favorite season. What is the temperature like? How much sunlight do you get each day?

Match each vocabulary term with its meaning. Write the letter on the blank beside it.

____ 1. planet

____ 2. asteroid

____ 3. orbit

____ 4. solar system

a. to travel in an oval path

b. a body of matter that orbits the Sun

c. the Sun, the nine planets, and their moons

d. a chunk of rock in orbit around the Sun

In the box below, draw a picture to illustrate the vocabulary terms. Use the words as labels.

© Pearson Education, Inc.

Notes for Home: Your child learned the vocabulary terms for Chapter 16.
Home Activity: Ask your child to use the drawing above to explain the meanings of the vocabulary terms. Talk about how planets move in the solar system.

◎ Compare and Contrast

Read the science article. Use the information to compare and contrast Mercury and Pluto.

Mercury and Pluto

Mercury and Pluto are the two smallest planets in our solar system. Both are rocky. Mercury has no atmosphere, and Pluto has almost none. But in many ways, they are different. Mercury is closest to the Sun, so it is very dry and hot. Because Pluto is farthest from the Sun, it is very cold. Mercury orbits the Sun in just 88 Earth days, but Pluto takes 248 Earth years to travel around the Sun!

Mercury

Pluto

Apply It!

In the graphic organizer on the next page, write ways the two planets are alike in the middle section. Write ways they are different on the left and the right.

Characteristics of Mercury	Both Mercury and Pluto	Characteristics of Pluto

Notes for Home: Your child learned how to use a diagram to show how two subjects are different and alike.
Home Activity: Work with your child to make a list of ways the Moon and the Sun are alike and different.

Notes

Name _____

Lesson 1: What are the parts of the solar system?

Before You Read Lesson 1

Read each statement below. Place a check mark in the circle to indicate whether you agree or disagree with the statement.

	Agree	Disagree
1. The Sun is the biggest, hottest star.	○	○
2. Nine planets make up the solar system.	○	○
3. Gravity makes planets orbit the Sun.	○	○

After You Read Lesson 1

Reread each statement above. If the lesson supports your choice, place a check mark in the *Correct* circle. Then explain how the text supports your choice. If the lesson does not support your choice, place a check mark in the *Incorrect* circle. Then explain why your choice is wrong.

	Correct	Incorrect
1. _____ _____	○	○
2. _____ _____	○	○
3. _____ _____	○	○

 Notes for Home: Your child has completed a pre/post inventory of key concepts in the lesson.
Home Activity: Ask your child to model the revolution and rotation of one of the planets in the solar system using a large ball and a small ball.

Reviewing Terms: Sentence Completion

Complete each sentence with the correct word or phrase.

_____ 1. A(n) _____ is a large body that revolves around the Sun. (planet, asteroid)

_____ 2. The Sun, nine planets, their moons, and other objects in orbit around the Sun make up _____. (the solar system, space)

_____ 3. An object's _____ is the path it takes around the Sun. (asteroid, orbit)

_____ 4. Chunks of rock that orbit the Sun are called _____. (asteroids, outer planets)

Reviewing Concepts: Sentence Completion

Complete each sentence with the correct word.

_____ 5. The Sun is a _____. (planet, star)

_____ 6. Planets are held in orbit by the Sun's _____. (gravity, plasma)

_____ 7. Mercury, Venus, Earth, and Mars are the _____ planets. (inner, outer)

_____ 8. The planets are divided into inner and outer planets based on their distance from the _____. (Moon, Sun)

Applying Strategies: Compare and Contrast

Use complete sentences to answer question 9. (2 points)

9. Name one way in which the Sun and the planets are similar. Name one way in which they are different.

_____

_____

_____

Lesson 2: What are the planets?

Before You Read Lesson 2

Read each statement below. Place a check mark in the circle to indicate whether you agree or disagree with the statement.

	Agree	Disagree
1. Mercury rotates slower than Earth.	○	○
2. Earth's atmosphere is important to life.	○	○
3. Jupiter and Pluto are gas giants.	○	○

After You Read Lesson 2

Reread each statement above. If the lesson supports your choice, place a check mark in the *Correct* circle. Then explain how the text supports your choice. If the lesson does not support your choice, place a check mark in the *Incorrect* circle. Then explain why your choice is wrong.

	Correct	Incorrect
1. _____	○	○
_____		
2. _____	○	○
_____		
3. _____	○	○
_____		

Notes for Home: Your child has completed a pre/post inventory of key concepts in the lesson.
Home Activity: Make flash cards with the names of the planets. Have your child place them in order from closest to farthest from the Sun and tell about each one.

Reviewing Concepts: True or False

Write **T** (True) or **F** (False) on the line before each statement.

_____ 1. The inner planets are gas giants.

_____ 2. Earth is the third planet from the Sun.

_____ 3. Mars is called the "red planet."

_____ 4. Earth can support life because of its temperature, atmosphere, and liquid water.

_____ 5. Earth's surface always stays the same.

_____ 6. The outer planets are much closer together than the inner planets.

_____ 7. Gas giants have rings around them.

_____ 8. Pluto is the smallest planet in the solar system.

Applying Strategies: Calculating

9. The distance across Earth is 12,750 kilometers. The distance across Venus is 12,000 kilometers. How much greater is the distance across Earth than the distance across Venus? Show your work. (2 points)

© Pearson Education, Inc.

Finding Patterns in Tables

Every planet rotates. Some planets rotate faster than Earth, and some rotate slower than Earth. Look at the information in the table. The numbers show how many times each planet rotates for every one rotation of Earth.

Planets		Revolution Time (Earth Days)
Inner Planets	**Mercury**	58.8
	Venus	244
	Earth	1.0
	Mars	1.029
Outer Planets	**Jupiter**	0.411
	Saturn	0.428
	Uranus	0.748
	Neptune	0.802
	Pluto	0.267

1. How long does it take Venus to spin once on its axis?

_____

2. Which planet rotates fastest?

_____

3. How do the inner planets compare to the outer planets in rotation?

_____

Notes for Home: Your child looked for patterns in a table.
Home Activity: With your child, search for an encyclopedia or magazine article on the solar system. Find a table comparing the planets in some way and look for a pattern.

Notes

Dear Family,

Your child is learning about the Sun, Earth, and the rest of the solar system. In the science chapter The Solar System, our class learned what the Sun is and how it makes heat and light. Students also found out how the planets move in space.

As students studied the characteristics of each planet, they also learned many new vocabulary words. Help your child to make these words a part of his or her own vocabulary by using them when you talk together about the solar system.

planet
solar system
orbit
asteroid

The following pages include activities that you and your child can do together. By participating in your child's education, you will help to bring the learning home.

Family Science Activity
Solar System Demonstration

Materials:

- large round ball (for example: a basketball or soccer ball)
- smaller round ball (for example: a tennis ball or rubber ball)

Steps

1 Place both balls near one another on a countertop. Explain to your child that the larger ball is the Sun and the smaller ball is Earth.

2 Explain that the part of Earth facing the Sun is experiencing daytime. The part of Earth not facing the Sun is experiencing nighttime.

3 Have your child turn Earth in a complete circle. How many hours does it take for Earth to make one complete rotation? (24 hours)

4 Now have your child move Earth around the Sun. How many days does it take for Earth to make one complete orbit, or circle? (365 days)

Workbook

Space Detective

Circle the words in the puzzle below.

Y	X	I	L	N	Z	E	O	T	V	M	K
C	A	P	S	A	P	L	A	N	E	T	O
B	A	I	W	O	O	S	A	T	Y	P	I
A	S	A	T	M	O	S	P	H	E	R	E
S	A	Q	I	J	Y	S	E	A	U	P	G
O	S	P	B	R	S	E	B	I	T	O	N
U	T	L	O	R	B	I	T	U	O	M	R
E	E	R	A	T	A	H	R	S	Y	O	A
P	R	L	M	U	I	R	P	T	R	V	O
R	O	U	O	I	D	T	A	E	T	I	R
S	I	D	P	L	A	M	T	E	A	T	T
U	D	Y	S	Y	R	E	V	O	L	V	Y

Word Bank

atmosphere	gravity	planet	solar system
orbit	asteroid	rotate	revolve

Planet Position

Write the names of the planets in their order from the Sun.

M _ _ _ _ _ _

V _ _ _ _

E _ _ _ _

M _ _ _

J _ _ _ _ _ _

S _ _ _ _ _

U _ _ _ _ _

N _ _ _ _ _ _

P _ _ _ _

Fun Fact

Use the word *moon* in many phrases. "To shoot for the moon" means to do something unusual. "Once in a blue moon" means very rarely. "Crying for the moon" means wanting something that is hard to get.

Name _____

Match each vocabulary term with its meaning. Write the letter on the blank beside the word.

_____ 1. technology

_____ 2. invention

_____ 3. tool

_____ 4. computer

a. something made for the first time

b. machine for storing, processing, and getting information

c. device made by people to do work more easily

d. using knowledge to make tools and new ways to do things

Use each of the vocabulary terms from above to complete the diagram. Write the word that fits in the blank in each sentence.

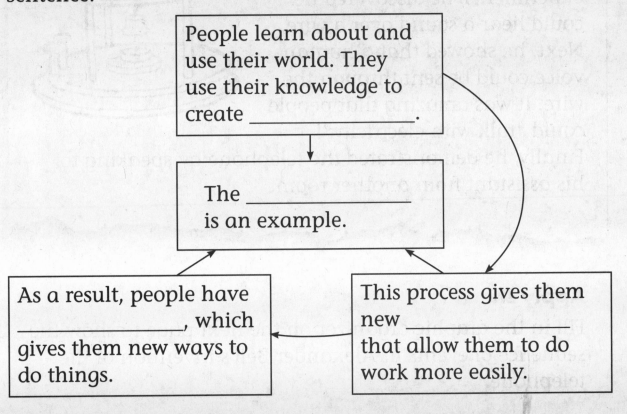

People learn about and use their world. They use their knowledge to create _____.

The _____ is an example.

As a result, people have _____, which gives them new ways to do things.

This process gives them new _____ that allow them to do work more easily.

Notes for Home: Your child learned the vocabulary terms for Chapter 17.
Home Activity: With your child, list some **tools** that make work easier, **inventions** that have changed our lives, and ways we use **technology** today.

Sequence

Read the science article.

Telegraph Wire

Alexander Graham Bell knew a lot about sound and music. He wondered whether more than one message could be sent over a telegraph wire. First, he experimented to try to send signals with different pitch over one wire. Then, during his experiments, he discovered he could hear a sound over a wire. Next, he showed that a human voice could be sent through the wire. It was amazing that people could "talk with electricity"! Finally, he demonstrated the telephone by speaking to his assistant from another room.

Apply It!

Fill in the graphic organizer on the next page to show the sequence of events in Alexander Bell's invention of the telephone.

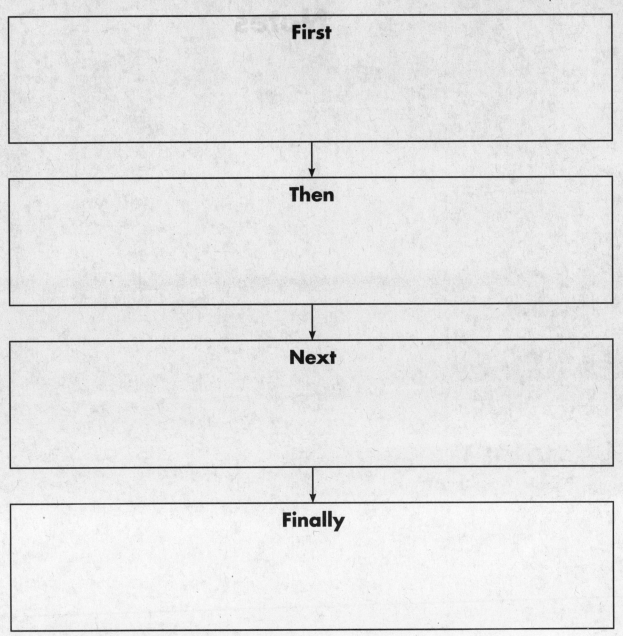

First

Then

Next

Finally

Notes for Home: Your child learned how to place events in logical, sequential order and use clue words signaling a sequence.
Home Activity: Ask your child to pick an electronic item he or she uses and explain the sequence of steps followed to use it.

Notes

Lesson 1: How does technology affect our lives?

Before You Read Lesson 1

Read each statement below. Place a check mark in the circle to indicate whether you agree or disagree with the statement.

	Agree	Disagree
1. People have used technology since the 1800s.	○	○
2. Inventions improve technology.	○	○
3. Technology systems work together.	○	○

After You Read Lesson 1

Reread each statement above. If the lesson supports your choice, place a check mark in the *Correct* circle. Then explain how the text supports your choice. If the lesson does not support your choice, place a check mark in the *Incorrect* circle. Then explain why your choice is wrong.

	Correct	Incorrect
1. _____	○	○
_____		
2. _____	○	○
_____		
3. _____	○	○
_____		

Notes for Home: Your child has completed a pre/post inventory of key concepts in the lesson.
Home Activity: With your child, brainstorm a list of inventions that make your lives easier and more pleasant. Talk about how and why each might have been invented.

Reviewing Terms: Matching

Match each description with the correct word. Write the letter on the line next to each description.

_____ 1. something that helps people do work more easily

_____ 2. the use of knowledge to design new tools and ways of doing things

_____ 3. something made for the first time

a. invention

b. tool

c. technology

Reviewing Concepts: True or False

Write **T** (True) or **F** (False) on the line before each statement.

_____ 4. People use technology to solve problems.

_____ 5. Technology was not used before the year 2000.

_____ 6. The systems in a house work together.

_____ 7. Ice boxes and refrigerators are both technology.

_____ 8. Technology will continue to change in the future.

Writing

Use complete sentences to answer question 9. (2 points)

9. Write one or two sentences that describe an invention you have used today.

_____

_____

_____

Lesson 2: What are some new technologies?

Before You Read Lesson 2

Read each statement below. Place a check mark in the circle to indicate whether you agree or disagree with the statement.

	Agree	Disagree
1. GPS uses a computer to figure out location.	○	○
2. Optical fibers improve communication.	○	○
3. TV was invented accidentally.	○	○

After You Read Lesson 2

Reread each statement above. If the lesson supports your choice, place a check mark in the *Correct* circle. Then explain how the text supports your choice. If the lesson does not support your choice, place a check mark in the *Incorrect* circle. Then explain why your choice is wrong.

	Correct	Incorrect
1. _____ _____	○	○
2. _____ _____	○	○
3. _____ _____	○	○

Notes for Home: Your child has completed a pre/post inventory of key concepts in the lesson.
Home Activity: Ask your child to choose a technology discussed in the lesson and tell why he or she thinks it is important.

Reviewing Terms: Sentence Completion

Complete the sentence with the correct word.

_____ 1. A _____ is a machine that stores, processes, and sends electronic information. (microwave, computer)

Reviewing Concepts: Sentence Completion

Complete each sentence with the correct word or phrase.

_____ 2. A _____ helps navigators find their location. (GPS, microwave)

_____ 3. Calculators, cameras, and digital watches all use _____. (computer chips, satellites)

_____ 4. Optical fibers are made of _____. (copper, glass)

_____ 5. The first transportation system used in the United States was _____. (highways, rivers)

_____ 6. _____ are the fastest way to carry cargo from one place to another. (Planes, Trains)

_____ 7. Microwaves are a form of _____. (radiation, radar)

_____ 8. _____ is a technology that allows TV screens to be large and flat. (LCD, Glass)

Applying Strategies: Math

9. There are about one million trucks in the United States today. Write the number *one million* in standard notation. (2 points)

_____

Lesson 3: How does technology help us get energy?

Before You Read Lesson 3

Read each statement below. Place a check mark in the circle to indicate whether you agree or disagree with the statement.

	Agree	Disagree
1. Running water is needed to produce electricity.	○	○
2. Wind and water produce most of our power.	○	○
3. Houses can use solar power.	○	○

After You Read Lesson 3

Reread each statement above. If the lesson supports your choice, place a check mark in the *Correct* circle. Then explain how the text supports your choice. If the lesson does not support your choice, place a check mark in the *Incorrect* circle. Then explain why your choice is wrong.

	Correct	Incorrect
1. _____ _____	○	○
2. _____ _____	○	○
3. _____ _____	○	○

Notes for Home: Your child has completed a pre/post inventory of key concepts in the lesson.
Home Activity: With your child, find out how the electricity you use is produced. Discuss some ways this method affects the environment.

Reviewing Concepts: True or False

Write **T** (True) or **F** (False) on the line before each statement.

_____ 1. Water was used for energy before electricity was invented.

_____ 2. Windmills and water-powered mills pollute the air and water.

_____ 3. Wind and water are renewable resources.

_____ 4. Hydroelectric power dams are used to make electricity.

_____ 5. The energy in burning coal can be used to make electricity.

_____ 6. Solar energy is the energy of wind.

_____ 7. Windmills change the kinetic energy of wind to electricity.

_____ 8. Through all of history, technology has been developed only in the United States.

Applying Strategies: Sequence

9. The steps of using coal to make electricity are shown below, but they are out of order. Use the clue words to write the steps in the correct order. (2 points)

Finally, pressure from steam turns wheels in electricity generators.
Next, heat is used to boil water.
First, coal is burned to produce heat.
Then boiling water makes steam.

_____

_____

_____

_____

Technology Time Line

In less than a hundred years, people went from the invention of the airplane to sending people into outer space. Look at the events listed in the chart. Mark each event on the time line below, then label it. The first item is done for you.

History of Flight

Year	Event
1903	First gas-powered, manned airplane flight
1926	First liquid-filled rocket launch
1958	First satellite orbits Earth
1969	First manned spacecraft lands on the Moon
1981	First flight of spacecraft that returns, lands, and can be reused
2000	First crew sent to International Space Station

first gas-powered manned airplane flight

1900   1920   1940   1960   1980   2000

1903

Notes for Home: Your child recorded events on a time line.
Home Activity: Help your child make a table showing important events in his or her life and the date they occurred. Then have your child transfer them to a time line like the one shown on this page.

Notes

Dear Family,

Your child is learning about how science and technology can affect our daily lives. In the chapter Science in Our Lives, our class has learned about how technology helps us solve problems. We have also learned about new technologies, such as Global Positioning Systems (GPS), and how they improve our lives.

Students have also learned many new vocabulary words. Help your child make these words a part of his or her own vocabulary by using them when you talk together about science and technological advances.

tool
technology
invention
computer

The following pages include activities that you and your child can do together. By participating in your child's education, you will help to bring the learning home.

© Pearson Education, Inc.

Family Science Activity
Technology Collage

Materials:

- magazines and newspapers
- scissors
- glue
- marker
- large sheet of paper or poster board

Steps

1. Look through magazines and newspapers for photographs and pictures that show examples of technology that is used today.

2. Have your child cut out pictures he or she would like to include in a collage.

3. Have your child arrange the pictures into a pleasing design; then glue or paste the pictures in place.

4. Ask your child to write a title for the collage; include captions for each picture that tell how people use these forms of technology in their daily lives.

Workbook

Vocabulary Practice

Write the answer for each riddle on the line. Each answer is a vocabulary word.

Word Bank
tool
technology
invention
computer

1. I can keep information so that you don't forget it. What am I?

_____

2. People created me. I am a telephone, an automobile, even a simple wheel. What am I?

_____

3. I am something you use to do work more easily. What am I?

_____

4. You use me to design new tools and new ways to do things. What am I?

_____

Tool Time

Invent a new tool. Draw it. Write sentences that tell how your tool helps you do work more easily.

_____

_____

_____

_____

What is the life cycle of a plant?

Growing plants need water, air, the right temperature, and sunlight. The pictures below show the life cycle of a peanut plant.

1. The part of a peanut you eat is a **seed**.

2. The seed grows a **stem** and a **root**.

3. The peanut plant grows leaves. It can start making sugar for food.

4. The **adult plant** makes seeds underground.

Answer the questions.

1. How many steps are there in the life cycle of a peanut?

   _____

2. What can a peanut plant do when it grows leaves?

   _____

3. Where does an adult peanut plant make its seeds?

   _____

4. What does a growing plant need?

   _____

How is a flower pollinated?

Bees, other animals, or wind pollinate a flower. This happens when they move pollen to the part of the flower that makes seeds. After a flower is pollinated, it grows seeds and fruit.

A flower's colorful petals may attract bees and other animals to the flower.

This bee is looking for food. It has pollen on its body. The bee moves pollen to the part of the flower that makes seeds.

Pollen put on the tip of this part helps form seeds here.

This part of the flower makes the pollen.

Answer these questions.

1. Why is the bee coming to the flower?

_____

2. What part of the flower attracts animals?

_____

3. What part of the plant makes seeds?

_____

4. How do bees, wind, and other animals pollinate a plant?

_____

5. What happens after a flower is pollinated?

_____

What are invertebrates?

Invertebrates do not have backbones. Invertebrates are the largest group of animals on Earth.

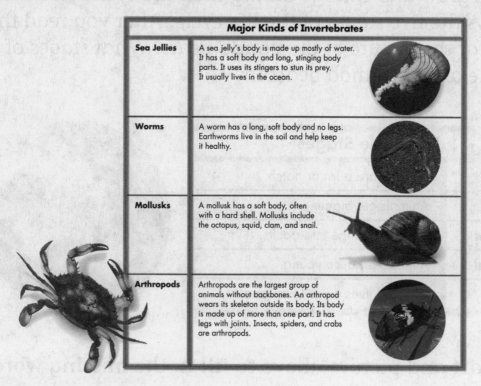

Major Kinds of Invertebrates		
Sea Jellies	A sea jelly's body is made up mostly of water. It has a soft body and long, stinging body parts. It uses its stingers to stun its prey. It usually lives in the ocean.	
Worms	A worm has a long, soft body and no legs. Earthworms live in the soil and help keep it healthy.	
Mollusks	A mollusk has a soft body, often with a hard shell. Mollusks include the octopus, squid, clam, and snail.	
Arthropods	Arthropods are the largest group of animals without backbones. An arthropod wears its skeleton outside its body. Its body is made up of more than one part. It has legs with joints. Insects, spiders, and crabs are arthropods.	

Answer the following questions.

1. What do all invertebrates have in common?

_____

2. What kind of invertebrate is an octopus?

_____

3. What do sea jellies, worms, and mollusks have in common?

_____

4. What kind of vertebrate is a fly?

_____

5. Which is the largest group of animals on Earth?

_____

How do animals grow and change?

All animals grow and change during their life cycle. The chart below shows the five stages of the life cycle. After you read the chart, look at the picture of the panda bears. What stages of the life cycle are the panda bears in?

Life Cycle Stages	
Birth	Animals are born or hatch.
Growth	Animals get bigger.
Development	Animals change into adults.
Reproduction	Animals produce young.
Death	Animals' lives come to an end.

Use the chart and picture above to fill in the missing words below.

1. The panda bear cub is in the (reproduction/birth)

   _____ stage of life.

2. The mother panda bear is in the (reproduction/

   development) _____ stage of life.

3. The _____ stage of life is when an animal changes into an adult.

4. Animals get bigger during the _____ stage.

5. Animals' lives come to an end at _____ .

What is in an ecosystem?

The environment of a living thing is everything that surrounds it. An ecosystem is all the living and nonliving things that interact with each other in an environment. Climate shapes each environment. Climate is the weather in a place all year.

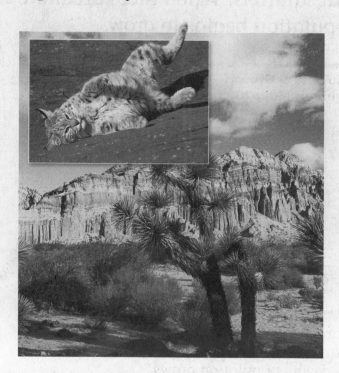

A Desert Ecosystem.
The Joshua Tree National Park is a desert ecosystem. The desert gets very little rain. It is hot during the day and cool at night. At night, the bobcat hunts for birds and other small animals. The sidewinder rattlesnake usually hunts at night for small animals to eat.

Answer these questions about the ecosystem above.

1. What is the climate like? Is it hot or cold? Wet or dry?

   _____

2. What living things do you see?

   _____

3. Is this ecosystem a good place for a bobcat? Why?

   _____

4. Why do you think the rattlesnake hunts at night?

   _____

© Pearson Education, Inc.

How do ecosystems change over time?

Ecosystems begin to change when one part of the ecosystem changes. For example, if it rains more than usual, plants grow more. Then, squirrels have more food to eat. The squirrel population grows. Coyotes eat squirrels. When there are more squirrels to eat, the coyote population begins to grow.

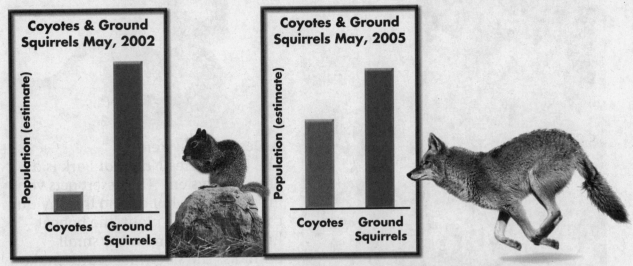

If there is more food, the squirrel population grows.

A larger squirrel population means more food for coyotes. The coyote population grows.

Answer these questions about the information above.

1. How can weather help change an ecosystem?

_____

2. What happens to the squirrel population when there are more plants?

_____

_____

3. Why does the coyote population grow?

_____

How do living things get energy?

Sunlight provides the energy for plants. Plants make their own food with energy from the Sun. They are producers. Animals get their energy from plants or from eating other animals. They are consumers.

A Food Chain

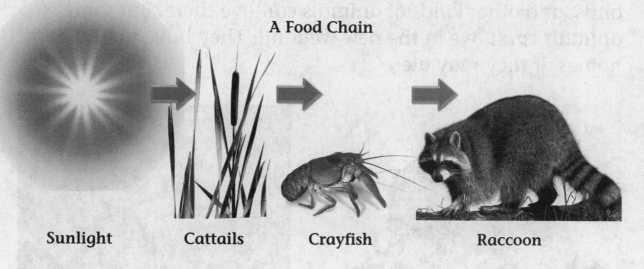

Sunlight　　　　Cattails　　　　Crayfish　　　　Raccoon

Answer these questions about the food chain above.

1. Where does the energy begin in this food chain?

   _____

2. Who are the producers in this food chain?

   _____

3. Who are the consumers in this food chain?

   _____

4. Do you think the raccoon is the end of this food chain? Explain.

   _____

   _____

How do beavers change the environment?

Plants and animals can change their environment. For example, beavers build dams of sticks and mud. Water backs up behind the dam and a new wetland habitat grows. Fish, birds, and other kinds of animals can live there. But some animals can't live in the new wetland. They have to find new homes or they may die.

Beaver

Beaver dam

Answer these questions.

1. How do beavers change their environments?

_____

2. What kind of new habitat grows around a beaver dam?

_____

3. What kinds of animals can now live in the wetland habitat?

_____

4. What happens to animals who can't live in the new wetland?

_____

Where do people get fresh water?

People need to drink fresh water. Only a small amount of the water on Earth is fresh water. Most fresh water is frozen as ice. Some fresh water comes from underground. This is called groundwater. A spring is a stream of groundwater that flows from underground. People also dig wells to get groundwater. We also get fresh water from lakes, rivers, and streams.

Most fresh water is frozen as ice. This iceberg is near Antarctica.

A spring is a stream of groundwater.

Answer these questions about fresh water.

1. Why do people need fresh water?

   _____

2. In what form is most of the fresh water on Earth?

   _____

3. Some fresh water flows from underground. What is this called?

   _____

4. What are some other ways people get fresh water?

   _____

   _____

Name _____

How does water move around Earth?

The water cycle is the movement of water from Earth's surface into the air and back again. Water changes during the water cycle. The Sun and wind cause water to evaporate and water to change into water vapor. Water vapor rises into cooler air and changes into water droplets. This is called condensation. When water droplets get too heavy, they fall to Earth as rain, snow, sleet, or hail.

Precipitation

Evaporation

Groundwater flow

Stream water flow

Answer these questions about the water cycle.

1. The picture shows water moving from Earth's surface to the air and back again. What is this called?

_____

2. What does water change into when it evaporates?

_____

3. What does water vapor change into when it rises?

_____

4. When water droplets get heavy, what happens?

_____

How can scientists measure weather?

Scientists use many tools to measure and describe weather, and help describe the atmosphere. The atmosphere has weight, so it presses down with a force called air pressure. Low air pressure often means weather will be cloudy or rainy. High air pressure often means clear skies.

Barometer
This tool measures air pressure.

Anemometer
This tool measures wind speed.

Wind Vane
This tool records the direction of the wind.

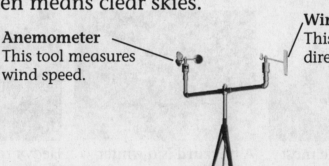

Answer these questions about measuring weather.

1. Which tool measures wind speed?

   _____

2. What is a wind vane used for?

   _____

3. What are all of these tools used for?

   _____

4. What causes air pressure?

   _____

5. If the air pressure is low, how will the weather probably be?

   _____

What are some dangerous storms?

Some storms can be dangerous. **Hurricanes** are huge storms that form over the ocean. Hurricanes have heavy rains, winds, and waves. **Tornadoes** are spinning columns of air that form beneath thunderstorm clouds. Tornadoes are much smaller than hurricanes, but can have stronger winds. A **blizzard** is a winter snow storm.

Hurricanes do the most damage when they move over land.

A **blizzard** is a winter storm with low temperatures and blowing snow.

Heavy rains and high waves can cause floods.

Most **tornadoes** have very strong winds.

Answer these questions.

1. When do hurricanes cause the most damage?

_____

2. What is a blizzard?

_____

3. What causes floods?

_____

4. How are tornadoes and hurricanes alike? Different?

_____

_____

_____

© Pearson Education, Inc.

What are the three main rock groups?

There are three main groups of rocks: **igneous, sedimentary,** and **metamorphic.** Each group contains many kinds of rocks.

Igneous

Sedimentary

Metamorphic

This granite is igneous rock. All igneous rock has grains. The grains can be large or small.

This shale is sedimentary rock. All sedimentary rock has layers.

This gneiss was once igneous rock with grains. The grains of gneiss are now layers. All metamorphic rocks changed from another kind of rock.

This slate was once sedimentary rock. The slate doesn't have layers like shale.

Answer these questions about rock groups.

1. What is an example of an igneous rock?

_____

2. What is an example of a sedimentary rock?

_____

3. In what way is a metamorphic rock different from the other groups?

_____

4. What kind of rock is shale? What can shale turn into?

_____

5. What kind of rock does gneiss come from?

_____

What are some properties of minerals?

A **mineral** is a natural material that forms from nonliving matter. Rocks are made up of minerals. You can compare minerals by **color**, **luster** (the way they reflect light), **streak** (the kind of mark they make), and **hardness**.

Properties of Minerals

Mineral	Color	Luster	Streak	Hardness
Mica This mineral breaks into flaky pieces when it is struck.	black, gray, green, violet	pearly on surfaces	white	can be scratched with a knife
Molybdenite This is one of the strongest minerals and is used very often. It resiststs heat.	silvery	metallic	bluish gray	can be scratched with a fingernail
Crocoite This mineral is often found in Australia.	reddish-orange	very shiny	orange-yellow	can be scratched with a coin

Answer these questions.

1. Which mineral is the softest? How do you know?

_____

_____

2. Which mineral would sparkle less in the sunshine? Why?

_____

3. What happens if you scratch Molybdenite against another rock?

_____

4. Which of the minerals would be safest to use near fires?

_____

What is weathering?

Any action that breaks rocks into smaller pieces is called **weathering**. There are many reasons why weathering happens. Freezing and thawing of water can break up rocks. Plants and animals can also cause weathering.

Weathering
As the roots in this tree grow,
they help to break up rock.

Answer these questions about weathering.

1. What is weathering?

_____

2. What are some of the reasons for weathering?

_____

3. How are the tree roots changing the rock?

_____

4. What kind of landform does this picture show?

_____

What is erosion?

After weathering happens, the materials can stay in place or move. When weathered material such as rock or sand moves, **erosion** takes place. Wind, water, glaciers, and gravity can cause erosion.

This is Bryce Canyon in Utah. Rain and melting snow caused erosion. The strange shapes are called "hoodoos."

Answer the following questions.

1. What caused erosion in this picture?

_____

2. What forces can cause erosion?

_____

3. What are the strange shapes in Bryce Canyon called?

_____

Name _____

What is conservation?

Some natural resources can be used up. Others can be used again and again. It's important that we protect our natural resources. When we do not waste or use up a natural resource, we practice **conservation**.

Water from homes is filtered through sand in ponds like these. Farmers use the recycled water for their orange trees.

Dirty water is piped into a wetland in Florida. It will become clean enough to be piped back into a river.

Answer these questions about conservation.

1. What natural resource do you see in both photographs?

   _____

2. How is conservation practiced in the wetlands?

   _____

3. How is water recycled for the trees in the photo on the right?

   _____

4. What are some ways you can help with water conservation?

   _____

   _____

How much is a year of trash?

A landfill is an area where trash is buried. The trash in a landfill never goes away. So, more and more area is needed for landfills.

What is in a Year's Worth of My Trash?	
Materials	**Mass (in kilograms)**
Paper	250
Plastic	80
Metal (steel cans)	40
Metal (aluminum cans)	10
Glass	40
Food scraps	80

Answer these questions.

1. What kind of trash do people throw away the most?

   _____

2. How much plastic and glass do people usually throw away in a year?

   _____

3. How can you help with paper conservation?

   _____

   _____

How do we measure volume?

The **volume** of an object is the amount of space it takes up. You can measure the volume of solid objects. The unit of measure for volume is the **cube unit**. To find the volume of a solid object, you measure how many cube units fit into it.

1 cubic unit

Fill the box with cubes to find its volume.

Answer these questions about measuring volume.

1. What is a cubic unit used for?

   _____

2. How is the volume of the box above measured?

   _____

3. What could you measure with cubic units in your classroom?

   _____

   _____

How do we measure volume?

We use the **cube unit** to measure volume.

12 cubes fill the box.
The volume is
12 cubic units.

Answer these questions.

1. How many cubes fill the box?

_____

2. How do you know the volume of a box?

_____

3. Is there another way you could measure the volume of the box?

_____

_____

Name _____

What are the three states of matter?

Matter can be in three different forms: solid, liquid, and gas. Physical changes such as changing the temperature, causes matter to change states. When matter changes from one state to another, it remains the same kind of matter.

States of Water

Ice is a **solid** and the particles are close together.

In **liquid** water, water particles slide past one another.

The water particles are far apart in the **gas** called water vapor.

Answer these questions about matter.

1. What is the same about the matter in the 3 containers?

   _____

2. What are the 3 different states of matter in the pictures?

   _____

3. What causes water to change form?

   _____

© Pearson Education, Inc.

Workbook

What is a chemical change?

In a chemical change, one kind of matter changes into another but usually cannot be changed back.

Rusting is a slow chemical change. Helped by water, the iron chain combines with oxygen gas in the air and slowly changes to rust. The rust cannot change back into iron.

Burning is a fast chemical change. When the sticks burn, the wood changes to gases and ashes. The sticks are no longer wood.

Answer these questions.

1. What do the picures both show?

_____

2. Which material shows slow chemical change?

_____

3. Which material shows a fast chemical change?

_____

4. Can either the iron or the wood change back to the kind of matter they were at first?

_____

How does force affect motion?

A push or a pull makes an object move.

The teams are pulling the rope in opposite directions. The team that pulls the rope with greater force will move the rope in its direction.

Answer these questions about force and motion.

1. What happens if you push or pull an object?

_____

2. How are the teams in the picture acting in the same way?

_____

3. How are the teams acting differently from one another?

_____

4. Which team will win this tug-of-war?

_____

Name _____

How do simple machines affect work?

Simple machines make it easier for people to do work. Inclined planes and wedges are two simple machines that help make work easier.

An inclined plane, or a **ramp**, is a slanting surface that connects a lower level to a higher level.

The axe head is a wedge. Wedges are used to split, cut, or fasten things.

Answer these questions.

1. What do simple machines do?

_____

2. What are two kinds of simple machines?

_____

3. What are wedges used for?

_____

4. What is an inclined plane?

_____

_____

Name _____

How does energy change form?

Energy comes in different forms. Here are five forms of energy you use every day.

Forms of Energy

Chemical	Kinetic	Electrical	Light	Thermal

This energy holds particles of matter together, especially in food.

This is the energy of moving objects. Moving parts in playground equipment use this energy.

This energy can pass through special wires. We use this energy to power appliances.

The Sun's rays are light energy. Plants make food with light energy.

We feel this energy as heat.

Answer these questions.

1. Which kind of energy does a seesaw at a playground use?

_____

2. Which kind of energy does a plant use to make food?

_____

3. Which kind of energy does a fire produce?

_____

4. Which kind of energy does a computer need to run?

_____

What is electrical energy?

Follow the path of the electric energy from one place to another.

1. Electric current flows along a path from the negative part of the battery.

2. Electricity flows through the circuit to the positive part of the battery.

3. On its way, current flows through the bulb. A wire in the bulb gets hot and glows. Electrical energy changes to heat and light energy.

Energy source

4. If you lift the lever on the switch, the circuit is broken, or open. The light turns off. Lower the level and the circuit is closed. The light turns on.

Switch

Answer these questions.

1. From where does electric current flow?

   _____

2. How does electrical energy change the bulb?

   _____

   _____

3. What happens if you lift the switch?

   _____

4. What would happen if you lower the lever?

   _____

What are vocal cords?

You are able to speak and sing because your vocal cords vibrate, or move back and forth. When you speak, your vocal cords tighten. They vibrate as air passes between them. Tight vocal cords make the pitch of your voice higher. Loose vocal cords make the pitch of your voice lower.

Vocal cords are the two pairs of thin tissue in the windpipe.

Answer these questions about vocal cords.

1. What are vocal cords?

   _____

2. Where are your vocal cords?

   _____

3. Place your fingers across your vocal cords. Hum lightly. What happens?

   _____

   _____

4. What happens to the pitch of your voice when your vocal cords tighten?

   _____

How do we hear?

Our ears receive sound waves that travel to our brain. The brain identifies the signals as sounds. This is how we hear.

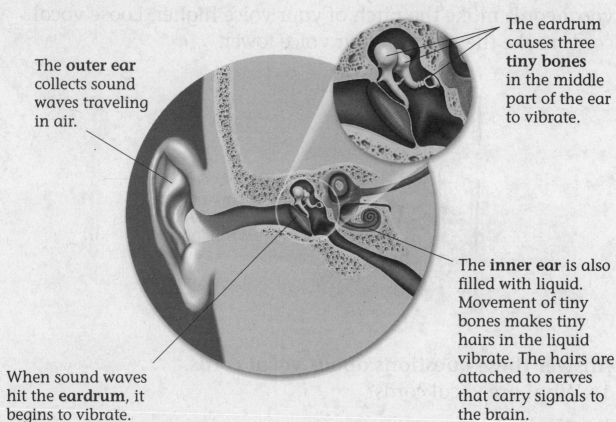

The **outer ear** collects sound waves traveling in air.

The eardrum causes three **tiny bones** in the middle part of the ear to vibrate.

When sound waves hit the **eardrum**, it begins to vibrate.

The **inner ear** is also filled with liquid. Movement of tiny bones makes tiny hairs in the liquid vibrate. The hairs are attached to nerves that carry signals to the brain.

Answer these questions.

1. In what order do the parts of the ear work in order for you to hear?

_____

2. What are the tiny hairs and liquid in the inner ear connected to?

_____

3. What happens to the eardrum when sound waves hit it?

_____

What are some patterns that repeat every day?

Earth is always moving. Earth spins, or rotates, on its axis. Earth makes one complete spin, or rotation, every 24 hours. During this time, half of Earth always faces the Sun. That half of Earth has day.

Earth makes one revolution every time it travels around the Sun. One revolution takes one year.

Answer these questions about Earth's movement.

1. Describe the two ways in which Earth moves.

_____

2. How long does it take for Earth to make one complete spin, or rotation?

_____

3. How long does it take for Earth to make one revolution around the Sun?

_____

What are the phases of the Moon?

The drawing below shows the Moon circling Earth. Half of the Moon is always lighted by sunlight. The lighted half of the Moon cannot always be seen from Earth. Each different way the Moon can be seen from Earth is a phase of the Moon. The pattern of the phases of the Moon takes about four weeks.

Phases of the Moon

New Moon
We cannot see the Moon.

Crescent
We see only a small piece of the lighted part of the Moon.

First Quarter
The Moon looks like a half circle.

Full Moon
We can see all of the lighted part of the Moon.

Answer these questions about the phases of the Moon.

1. What is a phase of the Moon?

   _____

2. What does the Moon look like during First Quarter?

   _____

3. Why can't we see the Moon during the New Moon phase?

   _____

   _____

4. How much of the Moon do we see during the Crescent phase?

   _____

How do planets in our solar system move?

Earth is one of nine planets in our solar system. Earth and the other planets travel, or revolve, around the Sun, which is the center of the solar system. Each complete path around the Sun is an **orbit**. The strong pull of gravity keeps planets in their orbits.

Answer these questions.

1. Which planet is closer to the Sun: Venus or Mars?

_____

2. Which planet is further from Earth: Mercury or Pluto?

_____

3. How is the Sun different from other planets?

_____

_____

4. What keeps the planets in orbit?

_____

What is Earth?

From space, Earth is blue, white, and brown. Blue water covers three fourths of Earth's surface. Clouds and large caps of ice appear white. The land appears brown. Earth supports life because of its warm temperatures, water, and atmosphere.

The coldest place on Earth is Antarctica.

The hottest place in the United States is Death Valley, California. A very hot 57°C (134°F) has been recorded there.

Earth

Answer these questions.

1. What color is Antarctica in this photograph? Why?

_____

2. What color is the hottest place in the United States? Why?

_____

3. How would you know where to point to an ocean?

_____

4. Will the cloud patterns swirling around Earth always look the same? Why not?

_____

5. What would happen to life on Earth if there were no water?

_____

Name _____

What are some technology systems in a house?

Parts of a house or apartment work together as a system that interacts.

Technology in a Home

Systems in a House
Framing
Roofing and waterproofing
Electrical
Plumbing
Heating/cooling

Answer these questions.

1. What house system do walls and floors belong to?

   _____

2. What object in the diagram is part of the heating/cooling system?

   _____

   _____

3. Name some appliances that use technology from the electrical system in your house.

   _____

© Pearson Education, Inc.

What is solar energy?

To meet our energy needs, people work hard to come up with new technologies and inventions. Solar energy is energy from sunlight. It does not cost very much.

Solar Energy

Solar energy warms water in this household appliance.

Solar panels concentrate the Sun's rays. This energy is changed into electricity.

Answer these questions about solar energy.

1. Where do you find solar panels?

_____

2. How do solar panels help turn lights on in a house?

_____

_____

3. How do solar panels help you take a hot bath or shower?

_____

_____

4. Why would it be hard to use solar panels for heat and electricity if you lived deep in woods?

_____

_____

© Pearson Education, Inc.

Picture Credits

Illustration

176 Peter Bollinger
193, 194 Jeff Mangiat
195, 196, 197 Paul Oglesby
199, 200 Robert Ulrich

Photographs

Every effort has been made to secure permission and provide appropriate credit for photographic material. The publisher deeply regrets any omission and pledges to correct errors called to its attention in subsequent editions.

Unless otherwise acknowledged, all photographs are the property of Scott Foresman, a division of Pearson Education.

167 © DK Images, © Nigel Cattlin/Holt Studios, © Nigel Cattlin/Photo Researchers, Inc., © Kenneth W. Fink/Photo Researchers, Inc. 168 © DK Images, Getty Images. 169 © Charles Melton/Visuals Unlimited, © Brad Mogen/Visuals Unlimited, © Dick Scott/ Visuals Unlimited, © DK Images, © Bettmann/Corbis. 170 © Danny Lehman/Corbis, © Robert PIckett/Corbis, © The Image Bank/Getty Images, © Brian Rogers/Visuals Unlimited. 171 Daniel J. Cox/Natural Exposures, © J. Eastcott/Y. Eastcott Film/NGS Image Collection. 172 Darren Bennett/Animals Animals/Earth Scenes, © Joseph Van Os/Getty Images. 173 © Chase Swift/Corbis, © Carol Havens/Corbis, © Frank Blackburn; Ecoscene/ Corbis, © D. Robert and Lorri Franz/Corbis. 174 Photo Researchers, Inc., © Richard H. Johnston/Getty Images. 175 © M. Timothy O'Keefe/Bruce Coleman Inc., © Wolfgang Kaehler/Corbis. 177 © Terry Renna/AP/Wide World Photos, © Boden/Ledingham/Masterfile Corporation, Digital Vision, © Allan Davey/Masterfile Corporation. 178 © Leonard Lessin/ Peter Arnold, Inc., © DK Images. 179 © DK Images, © Andrew J. Martinez/Photo Researchers, Inc. 180 © DK Images. 181 © Fred Whitehead/Animals Animals/Earth Scenes. 182 © William Manning/Corbis. 183 © Alan Towse/Ecoscene/Corbis, © Kevin Fleming/ Corbis. 188 © Richard Megna/Fundamental Photographs, © DK Images. 189 © Rolf Bruderer/Corbis, © Bob Daemmrich/Corbis, © DK Images. 190 © AGStockUSA, Inc./Alamy Images, © Henry T. Kaiser/Index Stock Imagery, © Lester Lefkowitz/Corbis, © Mark L. Stephenson/Corbis, © Mark C. Burnett/Photo Researchers, Inc. 196 © John Sanford/Photo Researchers, Inc. 198 NOAA, © Maria Stenzel/NGS Image Collection, © Bill Varie/Corbis. 200 Getty Images

Notes

What does the bold word in each sentence mean?
Circle the letter of the best answer.

1. The **deciduous** trees were bare by December 1.
   A. dead or dying   Ⓑ shedding leaves every year

2. **Seedlings** had sprouted from the seeds we planted.
   A. new leaves   Ⓑ small, new plants

3. Bees often **pollinate** flowers as they fly from plant to plant.
   Ⓐ move pollen to seed-making part
   B. remove pollen to make seeds

4. A pine tree is an example of a **coniferous** tree.
   Ⓐ describes trees that grow cones to make seeds
   B. describes plants with a strong scent

5. Seeds can **germinate** if they have the right amounts of water, light, and air.
   A. live a long time   Ⓑ start to grow

6. A new plant gets food from its **seed leaf** at first.
   A. green part of a seed   Ⓑ part of a seed that has food

7. We can learn about plants of the past by looking at **fossils**.
   Ⓐ marks left in rock   B. plants no longer alive

8. The root **system** of a plant takes in water and minerals and holds the plant in place.
   A. small parts   Ⓑ parts that work together

9. Many plants that once grew on Earth are now **extinct**.
   A. smaller   Ⓑ no longer alive

Notes for Home: Your child learned the vocabulary terms for Chapter 1.
Home Activity: Ask your child to show you illustrations in the book that help him or her understand the vocabulary terms. Use the words in sentences as you talk about the pictures.

Ⓒ Compare and Contrast

Read the paragraph.

Trees and Grasses

Trees and grasses are both plants. They both have leaves and root systems. Both need sunshine, water, and minerals. However, grasses are small, with soft stems and fine roots. Trees are large, with wood stems and large, deep roots.

Apply It!

How are trees and grasses the same and different? Use the information from the science article to fill in the graphic organizer on page 3.

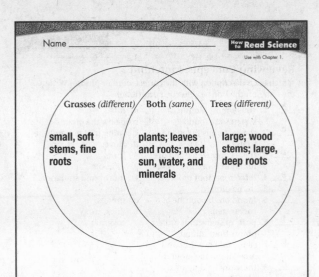

Grasses (different) — small, soft stems, fine roots

Both (same) — plants; leaves and roots; need sun, water, and minerals

Trees (different) — large; wood stems; large, deep roots

Notes for Home: Your child has learned how to compare and contrast living things.
Home Activity: Read the information on two different seed packets with your child. Discuss how the plants are the same and different in their growing requirements and habits.

Lesson 1: What are the main parts of a plant?

Before You Read Lesson 1

Read each statement below. Place a check mark in the circle to indicate whether you agree or disagree with the statement.

	Agree	Disagree
1. Roots take in food for plants.	○	✓
2. Leaves make sugar and oxygen for plants.	✓	○
3. Plants release water through leaves.	✓	○

After You Read Lesson 1

Reread each statement above. If the lesson supports your choice, place a check mark in the *Correct* circle. Then explain how the text supports your choice. If the lesson does not support your choice, place a check mark in the *Incorrect* circle. Then explain why your choice is wrong.

	Correct	Incorrect
1. _____	○	○
2. _____	○	○
3. _____	○	○

Notes for Home: Your child has completed a pre/post inventory of key concepts in the lesson.
Home Activity: Have your child compare different types of leaves on plants in and around your home. Together look at leaf parts through a magnifying glass.

Reviewing Terms: Sentence Completion

Complete the sentence with the correct word or phrase.

system 1. A plant's leaves are one kind of _____ because they have parts that work together. (shelter, system)

Reviewing Concepts: True or False

Write **T** (True) or **F** (False) on the line before each statement.

T 2. All living things need air and water.
F 3. Both plants and animals can make their own food.
F 4. The main parts of a plant are the roots, stems, leaves, and oxygen.
F 5. Plants use energy from the soil to make food.
T 6. Sugar and oxygen are made in leaves.
T 7. Some leaves protect plants from being eaten by hungry animals.
T 8. Leaves help plants in more than one way.

Applying Strategies: Measurement

Use complete sentences to answer question 9. (2 points)

9. Leaves come in many shapes and sizes. What tool would you use to measure the length of a leaf? Explain your choice.

I would use a metric ruler to measure the length of a leaf because a ruler is a tool for measuring lengths and distances.

Lesson 2: Why do plants need roots and stems?

Before You Read Lesson 2

Read each statement below. Place a check mark in the circle to indicate whether you agree or disagree with the statement.

	Agree	Disagree
1. Roots can store food for plants.	✓	○
2. Plant stems are like two-way pipelines.	✓	○
3. People eat roots and stems.	✓	○

After You Read Lesson 2

Reread each statement above. If the lesson supports your choice, place a check mark in the *Correct* circle. Then explain how the text supports your choice. If the lesson does not support your choice, place a check mark in the *Incorrect* circle. Then explain why your choice is wrong.

	Correct	Incorrect
1. _____	○	○
2. _____	○	○
3. _____	○	○

Notes for Home: Your child has completed a pre/post inventory of key concepts in the lesson.
Home Activity: Together with your child, look at vegetables in your kitchen. Have your child identify which are leaves, which are roots, and which are stems.

Reviewing Concepts: Matching

Match each description with the correct word or phrase. Write the letter on the line next to each description.

b 1. where most plant root systems are found
c 2. the materials taken in by roots
a 3. these carry water and are found in roots and stems
e 4. large roots that grow deep in the ground
h 5. found on the outside of a cactus stem
f 6. parts of stems that protect plants from animals
g 7. stems that are thin and grow along the ground
d 8. these are held up by a plant's stem

a. tubes
b. below the ground
c. water and minerals
d. leaves, flowers, and fruits
e. taproots
f. thorns and stinging hairs
g. stolons
h. thick, waxy covering

Writing

Use complete sentences to answer question 9. (2 points)

9. Name two ways a plant's stem system can help a plant to survive in its environment.

Sample: Some stems, like those of a cactus, are adapted to hold water in a desert environment to keep the plant from drying out. Some stems have thorns and stinging hairs to keep the plant from being eaten by animals.

Lesson 3: How are plants grouped?

Before You Read Lesson 3

Read each statement below. Place a check mark in the circle to indicate whether you agree or disagree with the statement.

	Agree	Disagree
1. Trees are flowering plants.	✓	○
2. Deciduous trees keep their leaves.	○	✓
3. Wind can pollinate a flower.	✓	○

After You Read Lesson 3

Reread each statement above. If the lesson supports your choice, place a check mark in the *Correct* circle. Then explain how the text supports your choice. If the lesson does not support your choice, place a check mark in the *Incorrect* circle. Then explain why your choice is wrong.

	Correct	Incorrect
1. _____	○	○
_____		
2. _____	○	○
_____		
3. _____	○	○
_____		

Notes for Home: Your child has completed a pre/post inventory of key concepts in the lesson.
Home Activity: Go for a walk with your child in your neighborhood or in a park. Ask your child to identify a deciduous tree, an evergreen, and a grass.

Reviewing Terms: Matching

Match each definition with the correct word. Write the letter on the line next to each definition.

__b__ 1. trees that lose their leaves in the fall   a. coniferous
__a__ 2. trees that grow cones to make seeds   b. deciduous
__c__ 3. to move pollen so a seed can form   c. pollinate

Reviewing Concepts: Sentence Completion

Complete each sentence with the correct word or phrase.

__Grasses__ 4. _____ are flowering plants that grow back from the roots each spring. (Grasses, Trees)

__seeds__ 5. The function of a flower is to make _____. (cones, seeds)

__pollen__ 6. In order for a seed to form, _____ must be moved from one part of a flower to another. (needles, pollen)

__flowers__ 7. The seeds of deciduous trees form in _____. (flowers, cones)

__flowering__ 8. Fruits form on some _____ plants. (coniferous, flowering)

Applying Strategies: Compare and Contrast

Use complete sentences to answer question 9. (2 points)

9. Describe one way in which seed cones and pollen cones are similar. Then describe one difference between them.
Sample: Seed cones and pollen cones are both found on coniferous trees. They are different because pollen cones are small and seed cones are large.

Lesson 4: How do new plants grow?

Before You Read Lesson 4

Read each statement below. Place a check mark in the circle to indicate whether you agree or disagree with the statement.

	Agree	Disagree
1. The seedling protects the seed.	○	✓
2. The seed leaf becomes a new plant.	○	✓
3. Sticky seeds are spread by animals.	✓	○

After You Read Lesson 4

Reread each statement above. If the lesson supports your choice, place a check mark in the *Correct* circle. Then explain how the text supports your choice. If the lesson does not support your choice, place a check mark in the *Incorrect* circle. Then explain why your choice is wrong.

	Correct	Incorrect
1. _____	○	○
_____		
2. _____	○	○
_____		
3. _____	○	○
_____		

Notes for Home: Your child has completed a pre/post inventory of key concepts in the lesson.
Home Activity: Gather different kinds of seeds from packets, fruit, or the outdoors. Ask your child how he or she thinks each seed is spread.

Reviewing Terms: Sentence Completion

Complete each sentence with the correct word or phrase.

__germinate__ 1. A seed can _____, or start to grow, when the conditions are right. (scatter, germinate)

__seed leaf__ 2. A new plant uses food stored in the _____. (seed leaf, seedling)

__seedling__ 3. A _____ is a plant that has just germinated. (seedling, flower)

Reviewing Concepts: True or False

Write **T** (True) or **F** (False) on the line before each statement.

__T__ 4. Some seeds are scattered by animals.
__F__ 5. A seed can germinate no matter what the temperature is.
__F__ 6. Coconuts are seeds that are scattered by the wind.
__T__ 7. Seeds are protected by a seed coat.
__F__ 8. All seeds are scattered in the same way.

Applying Strategies: Bar Graphs

9. Kendra planted seeds. She counted how many seeds germinated each day. Make a bar graph that shows Kendra's data. (2 points)
Bar graphs should show 5 seeds germinating on Monday, 3 on Tuesday, and 2 on Wednesday. Check to see that graphs have labeled axes and a title.

Day	Number of Seeds Germinating
Monday	5
Tuesday	3
Wednesday	2

Lesson 5: How are plants from the past like today's plants?

Before You Read Lesson 5

Read each statement below. Place a check mark in the circle to indicate whether you agree or disagree with the statement.

	Agree	Disagree
1. The first plants had no flowers or seeds.	✓	○
2. Living plants are exactly like extinct plants.	○	✓
3. A petrified fossil is made of rock.	✓	○

After You Read Lesson 5

Reread each statement above. If the lesson supports your choice, place a check mark in the *Correct* circle. Then explain how the text supports your choice. If the lesson does not support your choice, place a check mark in the *Incorrect* circle. Then explain why your choice is wrong.

	Correct	Incorrect
1. _____ _____	○	○
2. _____ _____	○	○
3. _____ _____	○	○

Notes for Home: Your child has completed a pre/post inventory of key concepts in the lesson.
Home Activity: Have your child compare a picture of a fern to the fossils of ferns shown on text page 22. Talk about ways they look the same and different.

Reviewing Terms: Matching

Match each definition with the correct word. Write the letter on the line next to each definition.

b 1. the remains or mark of a living
thing from long ago

a 2. kinds of plants that are no longer
alive anywhere on Earth

a. extinct
b. fossil

Reviewing Concepts: True or False

Write **T** (True) or **F** (False) on the line before each statement.

F 3. Fossils do not show anything about the kinds of plants that lived long ago.

T 4. Fossils form when rock replaces the parts of a plant.

F 5. Fossils form over a short period of time.

T 6. Some plant fossils are imprints.

F 7. Extinct plants are growing on Earth today.

T 8. Some plants alive today are similar to ancient ones.

Applying Strategies: Sequencing

Use complete sentences to answer question 9. (2 points)

9. Using the clue words in the sentences below, write the steps of fossil formation in the correct order.

Next, the plant was pressed in the mud.
Finally, the mud hardened into rock.
First, the plant died.
Then the plant rotted away.

First, the plant died. Next, the plant was pressed in the mud. Then the plant rotted away. Finally, the mud hardened into rock.

Elapsed Time

Jim will take care of the garden in July. The plants in the garden need to be watered every three days. They need to be weeded every seven days.

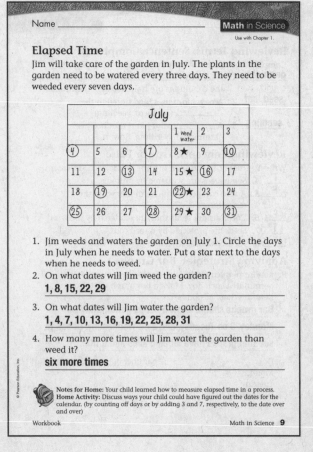

1. Jim weeds and waters the garden on July 1. Circle the days in July when he needs to water. Put a star next to the days when he needs to weed.

2. On what dates will Jim weed the garden?
1, 8, 15, 22, 29

3. On what dates will Jim water the garden?
1, 4, 7, 10, 13, 16, 19, 22, 25, 28, 31

4. How many more times will Jim water the garden than weed it?
six more times

Notes for Home: Your child learned how to measure elapsed time in a process.
Home Activity: Discuss ways your child could have figured out the dates for the calendar. (by counting off days or by adding 3 and 7, respectively, to the date over and over)

Choose a word to complete each sentence. Underline clues that helped you decide.

vertebrate	inherited	hibernate	pupa
adaptations	migrate	larva	traits

1. A dog, a fish, and a person are all examples of a
vertebrate, or an animal with a backbone.

2. An insect egg may hatch into a **larva**,
which eats a lot and grows fast.

3. **Adaptations**, such as sharp teeth or webbed feet,
help an animal survive where it lives.

4. **Traits** are body features passed on by an
animal to its young.

5. A trait that is always passed on from parents to offspring is
said to be **inherited**.

6. A caterpillar forms a hard shell around itself and becomes
a **pupa**. When it comes out, it will be an
adult.

7. Some animals **migrate** to the south for the
winter. There they can find food.

8. Other animals know when to **hibernate**, or
slow down their bodies and sleep a long time.

Notes for Home: Your child learned the vocabulary terms for Chapter 2.
Home Activity: Have your child use pictures in the text to provide examples that help define the vocabulary words. Action words can be acted out.

Sequence

Read the paragraph.

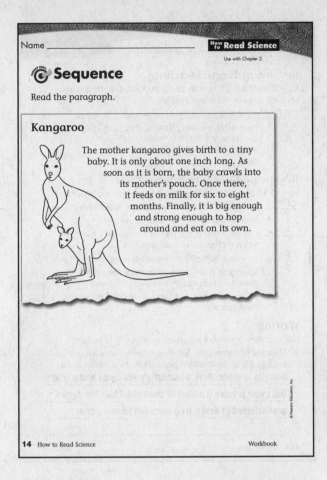

Kangaroo

The mother kangaroo gives birth to a tiny baby. It is only about one inch long. As soon as it is born, the baby crawls into its mother's pouch. Once there, it feeds on milk for six to eight months. Finally, it is big enough and strong enough to hop around and eat on its own.

Apply It!

What are the sequence of events in the paragraph about the kangaroo? Fill in the graphic organizer to show the correct order.

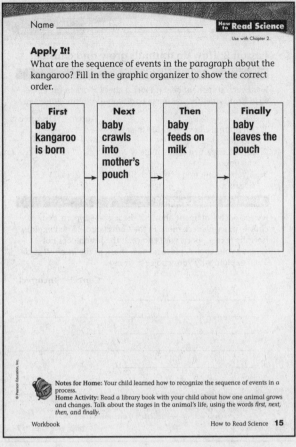

First	**Next**	**Then**	**Finally**
baby kangaroo is born	baby crawls into mother's pouch	baby feeds on milk	baby leaves the pouch

Notes for Home: Your child learned how to recognize the sequence of events in a process.
Home Activity: Read a library book with your child about how one animal grows and changes. Talk about the stages in the animal's life, using the words *first, next, then,* and *finally.*

Lesson 1: How are animals grouped?

Before You Read Lesson 1

Read each statement below. Place a check mark in the circle to indicate whether you agree or disagree with the statement.

	Agree	Disagree
1. There are many more invertebrates than vertebrates.	✓	○
2. All vertebrates have a backbone.	✓	○
3. Cats are vertebrates, but fish are not.	○	✓

After You Read Lesson 1

Reread each statement above. If the lesson supports your choice, place a check mark in the *Correct* circle. Then explain how the text supports your choice. If the lesson does not support your choice, place a check mark in the *Incorrect* circle. Then explain why your choice is wrong.

	Correct	Incorrect
1. _____	○	○
2. _____	○	○
3. _____	○	○

Notes for Home: Your child has completed a pre/post inventory of key concepts in the lesson.
Home Activity: Have your child cut out magazine pictures of animals and group them to show various ways they are similar.

Reviewing Terms: Sentence Completion

Complete the sentence with the correct word or phrase.

Traits 1. _____ are features of animals, like fish's gills or scales. (Traits, Needs)

vertebrates 2. _____ Cats and dogs are because they have backbones. (vertebrates, invertebrates)

Reviewing Concepts: Matching

Match each vertebrate with the correct group. Write the letter on the line next to each vertebrate.

b 3. snake   a. mammal
c 4. frog   b. reptile
a 5. dog   c. amphibian

Match each invertebrate with the correct group. Write the letter on the line next to each invertebrate.

c 6. octopus   a. arthropod
a 7. crab   b. worm
b 8. earthworm   c. mollusk

Applying Strategies: Calculating

9. On a visit to the zoo, Jennifer's class saw 20 species of fishes, 5 species of amphibians, 10 species of birds, and 12 species of mammals. How many species did they see altogether? Show your work. (2 points)

20 + 5 + 10 + 12 = 47 species altogether

Think, Read, Learn

Use with pages 44–47.

Lesson 2: How do animals grow and change?

Before You Read Lesson 2

Read each statement below. Place a check mark in the circle to indicate whether you agree or disagree with the statement.

	Agree	Disagree
1. All animals develop inside their mothers.	○	✓
2. A butterfly's first stage of life is the pupa.	○	✓
3. A very young frog acts much like a fish.	✓	○

After You Read Lesson 2

Reread each statement above. If the lesson supports your choice, place a check mark in the *Correct* circle. Then explain how the text supports your choice. If the lesson does not support your choice, place a check mark in the *Incorrect* circle. Then explain why your choice is wrong.

	Correct	Incorrect
1. _____	○	○
2. _____	○	○
3. _____	○	○

Notes for Home: Your child has completed a pre/post inventory of key concepts in the lesson.
Home Activity: Have your child compare photographs of himself or herself at different ages and note how he or she has changed while growing.

Workbook   Think, Read, Learn **17**

Lesson 2 Review

Use with pages 44–47.

Reviewing Terms: Matching

Match each definition with the correct word. Write the letter on the line next to each definition.

__a__ 1. the first stage of a butterfly's life cycle after hatching from an egg   a. larva

__b__ 2. the stage of a butterfly's life cycle when it is covered by a hard coating   b. pupa

Reviewing Concepts: True or False

Write **T** (True) or **F** (False) on the line before each statement.

__F__ 3. All animals have the same steps in their life cycles.

__T__ 4. Some animals start their lives as eggs.

__T__ 5. Development is the part of an animal's life cycle when it changes into an adult.

__F__ 6. An adult butterfly comes out of a larva.

__F__ 7. Mammals have more changes in their life cycle than insects or amphibians.

__T__ 8. When mammals are born, they drink milk from their mother.

Writing

Use complete sentences to answer question 9. (2 points)

9. Describe one similarity between a butterfly's life cycle and a frog's life cycle. Describe one difference between them.

Sample answer: Both a butterfly's life cycle and a frog's life cycle involve a series of changes. Their life cycles are different in that a frog does not form a pupa.

17A Lesson Review   Workbook

Think, Read, Learn

Use with pages 48–53.

Lesson 3: How do adaptations help animals?

Before You Read Lesson 3

Read each statement below. Place a check mark in the circle to indicate whether you agree or disagree with the statement.

	Agree	Disagree
1. Body parts are adaptations.	✓	○
2. Adaptations must be learned.	○	✓
3. When animals migrate, they sleep a long time.	○	✓

After You Read Lesson 3

Reread each statement above. If the lesson supports your choice, place a check mark in the *Correct* circle. Then explain how the text supports your choice. If the lesson does not support your choice, place a check mark in the *Incorrect* circle. Then explain why your choice is wrong.

	Correct	Incorrect
1. _____	○	○
2. _____	○	○
3. _____	○	○

Notes for Home: Your child has completed a pre/post inventory of key concepts in the lesson.
Home Activity: Discuss with your child some adaptations a pet (or a wild animal you can observe) has that help it survive.

Workbook   Think, Read, Learn **18**

Lesson 3 Review

Use with pages 48–53.

Reviewing Terms: Matching

Match each definition with the correct word. Write the letter on the line next to each description.

__b__ 1. a trait that helps animals meet their needs   a. inherited

      b. adaptation

__a__ 3. when animals move as the seasons change   c. migrate

      d. hibernate

__c__ 3. when animals move as the seasons change

__d__ 4. when an animal's body systems slow down to save energy

Reviewing Concepts: True or False

Write **T** (True) or **F** (False) on the line before each statement.

__T__ 5. A bird's bill is an adaptation that helps it meet its need for food.

__F__ 6. When a harmless animal looks like a poisonous one, it is called camouflage.

__F__ 7. An adaptation that allows an animal to blend in with its environment is mimicry.

__T__ 8. An instinct is a behavior that an animal is born knowing how to do.

Writing

Use complete sentences to answer question 9. (2 points)

9. Describe two ways that migrating helps animals survive.

Sample answer: Migrating helps an animal avoid cold weather. It also helps an animal meet its need for food.

18A Lesson Review   Workbook

Lesson 4: How are animals from the past like today's animals?

Before You Read Lesson 4

Read each statement below. Place a check mark in the circle to indicate whether you agree or disagree with the statement.

	Agree	Disagree
1. A fossil is an animal skeleton.	○	✓
2. Fossils show how life on Earth has changed.	✓	○
3. Today's desert may have once been a jungle.	✓	○

After You Read Lesson 4

Reread each statement above. If the lesson supports your choice, place a check mark in the *Correct* circle. Then explain how the text supports your choice. If the lesson does not support your choice, place a check mark in the *Incorrect* circle. Then explain why your choice is wrong.

	Correct	Incorrect
1. _____	○	○
2. _____	○	○
3. _____	○	○

Notes for Home: Your child has completed a pre/post inventory of key concepts in the lesson.
Home Activity: Have your child use modeling clay to create molds of animal parts, such as a paw or a shell. Talk about how fossils form in nature.

Reviewing Concepts: Sentence Completion

Complete each sentence with the correct word or phrase.

fossil   1. A(n) _____ is a sign of past life. (fossil, extinct)

hard   2. Only the _____ parts of an animal become a fossil. (hard, soft)

cast   3. A(n) _____ is formed when rock materials fill a fossil mold. (cast, amber)

amber   4. Hardened tree sap is called _____. (amber, bone)

actual bone   5. The fossils found in tar pits are _____. (actual bone, minerals)

no longer living   6. An extinct kind of animal is _____. (no longer living, found everywhere)

changed   7. Fossils show that Earth has _____ over time. (stayed the same, changed)

some   8. Fossils show that _____ animals today resemble extinct animals. (some, all)

Applying Strategies: Sequencing

9. Some insects are preserved in amber. The steps are shown here out of order. Using the clue words in the sentences, write the steps in the correct order. (2 points)

Next, the sap completely covers the insect.
Finally, the sap turns into amber.
First, an insect is trapped in sticky sap.

First, an insect is trapped in sticky sap.

Next, the sap completely covers the insect.

Finally, the sap turns into amber.

Comparing Animal Traits

A graph helps you compare numbers and amounts. Read the graph. Then answer the questions.

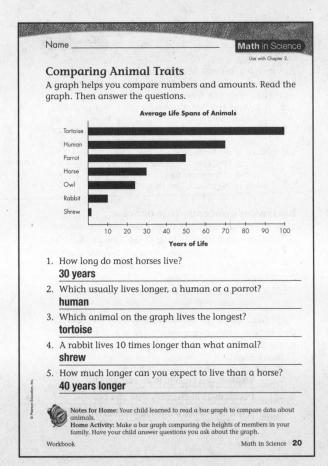

1. How long do most horses live?
30 years

2. Which usually lives longer, a human or a parrot?
human

3. Which animal on the graph lives the longest?
tortoise

4. A rabbit lives 10 times longer than what animal?
shrew

5. How much longer can you expect to live than a horse?
40 years longer

Notes for Home: Your child learned to read a bar graph to compare data about animals.
Home Activity: Make a bar graph comparing the heights of members in your family. Have your child answer questions you ask about the graph.

Use the words to fill in the map and show how the words are related to each other.

| environment | desert | ecosystem | grassland |
| population | tundra | community | wetland |

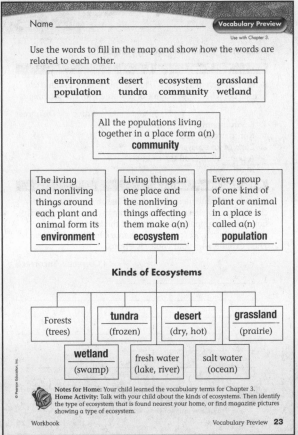

Notes for Home: Your child learned the vocabulary terms for Chapter 3.
Home Activity: Talk with your child about the kinds of ecosystems. Then identify the type of ecosystem that is found nearest your home, or find magazine pictures showing a type of ecosystem.

© Pearson Education, Inc.

Name _____

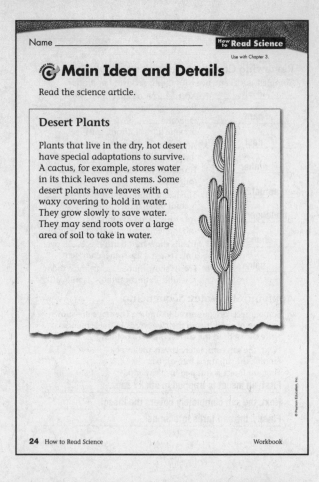

Main Idea and Details

Read the science article.

Desert Plants

Plants that live in the dry, hot desert have special adaptations to survive. A cactus, for example, stores water in its thick leaves and stems. Some desert plants have leaves with a waxy covering to hold in water. They grow slowly to save water. They may send roots over a large area of soil to take in water.

Name _____

Apply It!

In the outer squares, write details that support the main idea in the center circle.

Wording may vary slightly.

Store water in leaves and stems		Covering on leaves holds in water
	Desert plants are adapted to survive.	
Grow slowly to use less water		Have a large root system to get water

Notes for Home: Your child learned to identify details that support a main idea.
Home Activity: Read an article about plants or animals with your child. State one main idea of the article. Have your child point out details that support that main idea.

Name _____

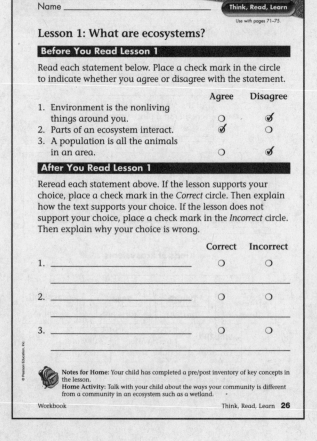

Think, Read, Learn
Use with pages 71–75.

Lesson 1: What are ecosystems?

Before You Read Lesson 1

Read each statement below. Place a check mark in the circle to indicate whether you agree or disagree with the statement.

	Agree	Disagree
1. Environment is the nonliving things around you.	○	✓
2. Parts of an ecosystem interact.	✓	○
3. A population is all the animals in an area.	○	✓

After You Read Lesson 1

Reread each statement above. If the lesson supports your choice, place a check mark in the *Correct* circle. Then explain how the text supports your choice. If the lesson does not support your choice, place a check mark in the *Incorrect* circle. Then explain why your choice is wrong.

	Correct	Incorrect
1. _____	○	○
2. _____	○	○
3. _____	○	○

Notes for Home: Your child has completed a pre/post inventory of key concepts in the lesson.
Home Activity: Talk with your child about the ways your community is different from a community in an ecosystem such as a wetland.

Name _____

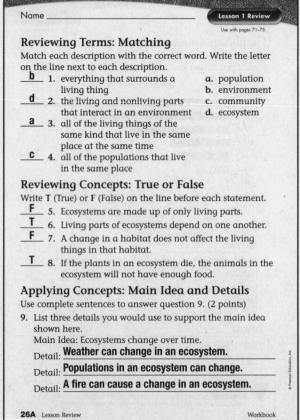

Lesson 1 Review
Use with pages 71–75.

Reviewing Terms: Matching

Match each description with the correct word. Write the letter on the line next to each description.

__b__ 1. everything that surrounds a living thing

__d__ 2. the living and nonliving parts that interact in an environment

__a__ 3. all of the living things of the same kind that live in the same place at the same time

__c__ 4. all of the populations that live in the same place

a. population
b. environment
c. community
d. ecosystem

Reviewing Concepts: True or False

Write **T** (True) or **F** (False) on the line before each statement.

__F__ 5. Ecosystems are made up of only living parts.

__T__ 6. Living parts of ecosystems depend on one another.

__F__ 7. A change in a habitat does not affect the living things in that habitat.

__T__ 8. If the plants in an ecosystem die, the animals in the ecosystem will not have enough food.

Applying Concepts: Main Idea and Details

Use complete sentences to answer question 9. (2 points)

9. List three details you would use to support the main idea shown here.

Main Idea: Ecosystems change over time.

Detail: **Weather can change in an ecosystem.**

Detail: **Populations in an ecosystem can change.**

Detail: **A fire can cause a change in an ecosystem.**

Lesson 2: Which ecosystems have few trees?

Before You Read Lesson 2

Read each statement below. Place a check mark in the circle to indicate whether you agree or disagree with the statement.

	Agree	Disagree
1. A grassland is a prairie.	☑	○
2. A desert is hot by day and cold by night.	☑	○
3. A tundra is too cold for big animals.	○	☑

After You Read Lesson 2

Reread each statement above. If the lesson supports your choice, place a check mark in the *Correct* circle. Then explain how the text supports your choice. If the lesson does not support your choice, place a check mark in the *Incorrect* circle. Then explain why your choice is wrong.

	Correct	Incorrect
1. _____	○	○
2. _____	○	○
3. _____	○	○

Notes for Home: Your child has completed a pre/post inventory of key concepts in the lesson.
Home Activity: Identify a land ecosystem found in your area. Together list the plants, animals, and objects that you and your child have seen there.

Reviewing Terms: Matching

Match each description with the correct word. Write the letter on the line next to each description.

__c__ 1. a land ecosystem with grasses and flowering plants
__b__ 2. a land ecosystem that gets very little rain
__a__ 3. a cold, dry land ecosystem

a. tundra
b. desert
c. grassland

Reviewing Concepts: Sentence Completion

Complete each sentence with the correct word.

__deep__ 4. Grasses survive in grasslands because they have _____ roots. (deep, shallow).

__deserts__ 5. Cactuses are plants found in _____. (deserts, grasslands)

__rainfall__ 6. Desert plants can live with very little _____. (sunlight, rainfall)

__tundra__ 7. Winters in the _____ are long and cold. (desert, tundra)

__frozen__ 8. In the tundra, soil below the surface stays _____ all year. (wet, frozen)

Applying Strategies: Compare and Contrast

Use complete sentences to answer question 9. (2 points)

9. Name one way in which deserts, tundra, and grasslands are all alike and one way in which they are different.

Sample: All three of these ecosystems are dry ecosystems that do not get much rainfall. These ecosystems are different because they have different average temperatures.

Lesson 3: What are some forest ecosystems?

Before You Read Lesson 3

Read each statement below. Place a check mark in the circle to indicate whether you agree or disagree with the statement.

	Agree	Disagree
1. Tropical forests lie near the equator.	☑	○
2. Trees in deciduous forests drop their leaves in fall.	☑	○
3. Coniferous forests get the most rain.	○	☑

After You Read Lesson 3

Reread each statement above. If the lesson supports your choice, place a check mark in the *Correct* circle. Then explain how the text supports your choice. If the lesson does not support your choice, place a check mark in the *Incorrect* circle. Then explain why your choice is wrong.

	Correct	Incorrect
1. _____	○	○
2. _____	○	○
3. _____	○	○

Notes for Home: Your child has completed a pre/post inventory of key concepts in the lesson.
Home Activity: With your child, observe some evergreen needles and some broadleaf leaves. Ask your child to tell how they are different.

Reviewing Concepts: Matching

Match each description with the correct kind of forest. Write the letter on the line next to each description. You can use each answer more than once.

__a__ 1. These grow mainly in northern North America, Europe, and Asia.
__b__ 2. Oak, maple, and beech trees are found in these.
__c__ 3. These have a climate that is warm and rainy all year long.
__a__ 4. Spruce, fir, and pine trees are found in these.
__a__ 5. Trees with leaves that look like needles are found in these.
__a__ 6. Mosses and lichens are some of the things that can live on the floor of these.
__c__ 7. These grow near the equator.
__b__ 8. Sunlight reaches the forest floor during a part of the year in these.

a. coniferous forests
b. deciduous forests
c. tropical forests

Applying Strategies: Converting Units

9. A tropical rainforest gets an average of 300 centimeters of rain each year. How many meters of rain is this? There are 100 centimeters in 1 meter. Show your work. (2 points)

300 cm × 100 = 3 m; A rainforest receives an average of 3 meters of rain each year.

© Pearson Education, Inc.

Use with pages 86–89.

Lesson 4: What are water ecosystems?

Before You Read Lesson 4

Read each statement below. Place a check mark in the circle to indicate whether you agree or disagree with the statement.

	Agree	Disagree
1. A wetland is a freshwater ecosystem.	✓	○
2. Most life in the oceans is at the bottom.	○	✓
3. Saltwater ecosystems cover most of the world.	✓	○

After You Read Lesson 4

Reread each statement above. If the lesson supports your choice, place a check mark in the *Correct* circle. Then explain how the text supports your choice. If the lesson does not support your choice, place a check mark in the *Incorrect* circle. Then explain why your choice is wrong.

	Correct	Incorrect
1. _____	○	○
_____		
2. _____	○	○
_____		
3. _____	○	○
_____		

Notes for Home: Your child has completed a pre/post inventory of key concepts in the lesson.
Home Activity: With your child, observe an aquarium (or read about setting one up). Together list the things needed for this freshwater ecosystem.

Workbook   Think, Read, Learn **29**

Use with pages 86–89.

Reviewing Terms: Sentence Completion

Complete each sentence with the correct word or phrase.

wetland 1. A low land covered by water at least part of the year is a _____. (wetland, tropical forest)

Reviewing Concepts: True or False

Write **T** (True) or **F** (False) on the line before each statement.

F 2. Lakes, ponds, and rivers are usually saltwater ecosystems.

T 3. Rivers and streams are moving water.

F 4. Water flows very quickly through the Everglades in Florida.

F 5. Animals do not live in the Everglades.

T 6. Ocean water is salt water.

F 7. Most living things in the ocean live at the very bottom.

T 8. Salt marshes form where river water mixes with ocean water.

Writing

Use complete sentences to answer question 9. (2 points)

9. Describe two ways that wetlands are important to animals.
Wetlands are a habitat in which animals live. Many plants grow in wetlands, and animals use these plants for food.

29A Lesson Review   Workbook

Use with Chapter 3.

Comparing Data

Look at the graph. Use it to answer the questions.

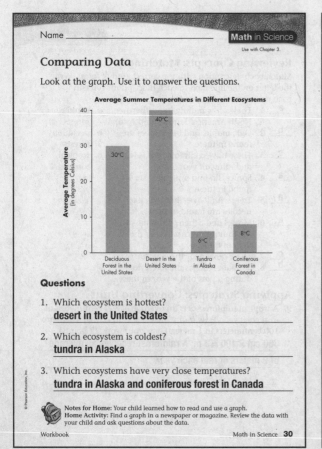

Average Summer Temperatures in Different Ecosystems

Average Temperature (in degrees Celsius)

- Deciduous Forest in the United States: 30°C
- Desert in the United States: 40°C
- Tundra in Alaska: 6°C
- Coniferous Forest in Canada: 8°C

Questions

1. Which ecosystem is hottest?
desert in the United States

2. Which ecosystem is coldest?
tundra in Alaska

3. Which ecosystems have very close temperatures?
tundra in Alaska and coniferous forest in Canada

Notes for Home: Your child learned how to read and use a graph.
Home Activity: Find a graph in a newspaper or magazine. Review the data with your child and ask questions about the data.

Workbook   Math in Science **30**

Use with Chapter 4.

Think about each word or set of words. Write the words to complete the outline.

I. germs

   A. What do they do? Germs cause **disease** .

   B. Examples of germs: **viruses, bacteria**

II. producer, consumer, predator, prey

   A. How do they get food? **Producers** make their own food. **Consumers** eat food.

   B. Who eats whom? A **predator** eats other animals, which are called **prey** .

III. herbivore, carnivore, omnivore

   A. How are they alike? They are all types of **consumers**

   B. How are they different? **Herbivores** eat only plants. **Carnivores** eat only animals. **Omnivores** eat both plants and animals.

IV. competition

   A. What is it? **two or more living things trying to use the same resource**

   B. When does it happen? **when living things in one area must have the same food, space, or mates**

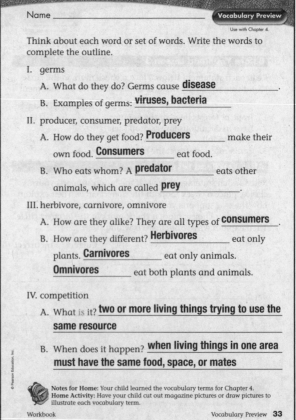

Notes for Home: Your child learned the vocabulary terms for Chapter 4.
Home Activity: Have your child cut out magazine pictures or draw pictures to illustrate each vocabulary term.

Workbook   Vocabulary Preview **33**

⊙ Draw Conclusions

Read the paragraph.

Jose Becomes Ill

Jose is beginning to get a fever and a sore throat. Last week, his little sister had a cold. They usually play with the same toys at home.

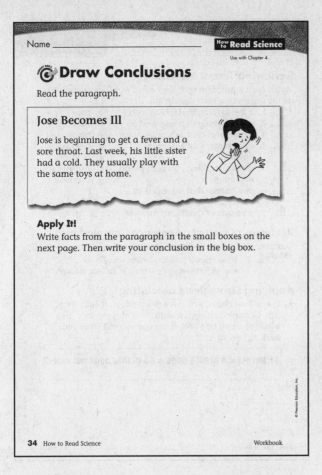

Apply It!

Write facts from the paragraph in the small boxes on the next page. Then write your conclusion in the big box.

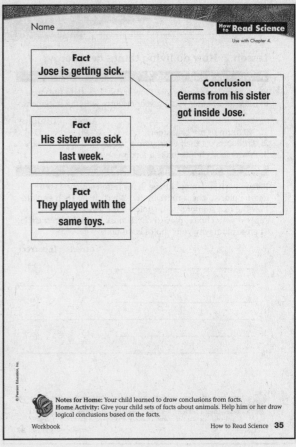

Fact	Conclusion
Jose is getting sick.	Germs from his sister got inside Jose.
His sister was sick last week.	
They played with the same toys.	

Notes for Home: Your child learned to draw conclusions from facts.
Home Activity: Give your child sets of facts about animals. Help him or her draw logical conclusions based on the facts.

Lesson 1: How do living things interact?

Before You Read Lesson 1

Read each statement below. Place a check mark in the circle to indicate whether you agree or disagree with the statement.

	Agree	Disagree
1. Animals may live in groups to protect each other.	✓	○
2. A bee visits a flower, and both benefit.	✓	○
3. Different kinds of living things do not help each other.	○	✓

After You Read Lesson 1

Reread each statement above. If the lesson supports your choice, place a check mark in the *Correct* circle. Then explain how the text supports your choice. If the lesson does not support your choice, place a check mark in the *Incorrect* circle. Then explain why your choice is wrong.

	Correct	Incorrect
1. _____	○	○
2. _____	○	○
3. _____	○	○

Notes for Home: Your child has completed a pre/post inventory of key concepts in the lesson.
Home Activity: Together observe an animal interaction, such as a pet getting food from you. Talk about how the interaction helps the animal(s) survive.

Reviewing Concepts: Matching

Match the examples with the correct description of the way living things interact. Write the letter on the line next to each description. You can use each answer more than once.

__a__ 1. members of a herd protecting each other

__c__ 2. a cleaner fish getting food when it cleans a larger fish

__a__ 3. a bee "dancing" to show other bees where flowers are

__b__ 4. a tree helping a flower get light, the flower does not help or harm the tree

__a__ 5. a prairie dog whistling to warn its group of predators

__c__ 6. a bee getting food when it pollinates a flower

__b__ 7. barnacles living on whales, the whales are not helped or harmed

__c__ 8. a moth pollinating a yucca plant and laying its eggs in the plant

a. helping in groups

b. one kind helping another

c. two kinds helping each other

Applying Concepts: Draw Conclusions

Use complete sentences to answer question 9. (2 points)

9. Read the three facts below. Then write a conclusion that is supported by the facts.

Fact 1: Sometimes animals help others in their group.

Fact 2: Sometimes one kind of animal helps another kind.

Fact 3: Sometimes two kinds of animals help each other.

Conclusion: **Sample : Animals have different ways of helping one another.**

© Pearson Education, Inc.

Lesson 2: How do living things get energy?

Before You Read Lesson 2

Read each statement below. Place a check mark in the circle to indicate whether you agree or disagree with the statement.

	Agree	Disagree
1. All animals are consumers.	✓	○
2. Producers get their energy from food.	○	✓
3. Many food chains make a food web.	✓	○

After You Read Lesson 2

Reread each statement above. If the lesson supports your choice, place a check mark in the *Correct* circle. Then explain how the text supports your choice. If the lesson does not support your choice, place a check mark in the *Incorrect* circle. Then explain why your choice is wrong.

	Correct	Incorrect
1. _____	○	○
2. _____	○	○
3. _____	○	○

Notes for Home: Your child has completed a pre/post inventory of key concepts in the lesson.
Home Activity: List some foods your family has eaten today. Have your child classify them as plant or animal. Talk about where each got its energy from.

Reviewing Terms: Matching

Match each description with the correct word. Write the letter on the line next to each description.

_e_ 1. a living thing that makes food	a. prey
_b_ 2. a living thing that eats food	b. consumer
_f_ 3. a consumer that eats only plants	c. omnivore
_g_ 4. a consumer that eats only animals	d. predator
_c_ 5. a consumer that eats both plants and animals	e. producer
_a_ 6. any animal that is hunted by others for food	f. herbivore
_d_ 7. a consumer that hunts for food	g. carnivore

Reviewing Concepts: Sentence Completion

Complete the sentence with the correct word.

energy 8. Food chains and food webs show how _____ moves between living things. (water, energy)

Applying Strategies: Calculating

9. In one food chain, ferrets eat prairie dogs. If each ferret eats 4 prairie dogs each month, how many prairie dogs would be eaten by 11 ferrets in one month? Show your work. (2 points)

> **11 ferrets × 4 prairie dogs = 44 prairie dogs per month**

Lesson 3: How do living things compete?

Before You Read Lesson 3

Read each statement below. Place a check mark in the circle to indicate whether you agree or disagree with the statement.

	Agree	Disagree
1. Animals compete, but plants do not.	○	✓
2. Two predators might compete for prey.	✓	○
3. Living things compete for food, water, and space.	✓	○

After You Read Lesson 3

Reread each statement above. If the lesson supports your choice, place a check mark in the *Correct* circle. Then explain how the text supports your choice. If the lesson does not support your choice, place a check mark in the *Incorrect* circle. Then explain why your choice is wrong.

	Correct	Incorrect
1. _____	○	○
2. _____	○	○
3. _____	○	○

Notes for Home: Your child has completed a pre/post inventory of key concepts in the lesson.
Home Activity: Observe some plants near your home. Discuss with your child how they are competing for the same space, food, and water and predict which will win.

Reviewing Terms: Sentence Completion

Complete each sentence with the correct word.

competition 1. When two or more living things need the same resources, they are in _____ with one another. (cooperation, competition)

Reviewing Concepts: True or False

Write **T** (True) or **F** (False) on the line before each statement.

- **T** 2. Living things compete for many kinds of resources.
- **F** 3. Animals do not compete for mates.
- **T** 4. Animals that are good predators pass those traits to their young.
- **F** 5. Prey often compete to get predators.
- **T** 6. Sometimes people and animals compete for space.
- **T** 7. Some living things compete for oxygen.
- **T** 8. Competition between animals sometimes follows cycles.

Writing

Use complete sentences to answer question 9. (2 points)

9. Write a short paragraph that describes two kinds of birds competing for a resource they both need to survive.

> **Sample paragraph: Birds build nests. If two kinds of birds build nests in the same tree, the birds will compete for space. The kind of bird that builds its nests earliest in the year will probably get the most space. The other birds might have to move or they might not get the space they need to survive.**

© Pearson Education, Inc.

Lesson 4: How do environments change?

Before You Read Lesson 4

Read each statement below. Place a check mark in the circle to indicate whether you agree or disagree with the statement.

	Agree	Disagree
1. Living things can change their environment.	✓	○
2. Fire destroys a forest forever.	○	✓
3. Environment changes often occur in patterns.	✓	○

After You Read Lesson 4

Reread each statement above. If the lesson supports your choice, place a check mark in the *Correct* circle. Then explain how the text supports your choice. If the lesson does not support your choice, place a check mark in the *Incorrect* circle. Then explain why your choice is wrong.

	Correct	Incorrect
1. _____	○	○
2. _____	○	○
3. _____	○	○

Notes for Home: Your child has completed a pre/post inventory of key concepts in the lesson.
Home Activity: Point out a community environment that has changed, such as a construction site. Ask your child how this change affected the organisms that live there.

Workbook   Think, Read, Learn **39**

Reviewing Terms: Sentence Completion

Complete each sentence with the correct word.

decomposer 1. A living thing that breaks down waste and living things that have died is a _____. (decomposer, decay)

Decay 2. _____ is the process of breaking down waste and living things that have died. (Decomposer, Decay)

Reviewing Concepts: Matching

Living things and natural events can cause environments to change. For each description of change listed below, show whether it is a change caused by a living thing or a natural event. You can use each answer more than once.

b 3. A volcano erupts and kills plants in an environment.

b 4. A hurricane knocks down trees.

b 5. A forest fire burns plants and trees.

a 6. A person chops down trees to make space to build a house.

b 7. A drought causes many plants to die.

a 8. A beaver's dam floods an area.

a. a living thing
b. a natural event

Applying Strategies: Cause and Effect

Use complete sentences to answer question 9. (2 points)

9. Write three causes of environmental change.

Cause: **humans cutting down trees**

Cause: **forest fires burning in an area or a volcano erupting**

Cause: **a hurricane washing away plants and trees**

Effect: An environment is changed.

39A Lesson Review   Workbook

Lesson 5: What is a healthy environment for people?

Before You Read Lesson 5

Read each statement below. Place a check mark in the circle to indicate whether you agree or disagree with the statement.

	Agree	Disagree
1. Food and water are all people need to live.	○	✓
2. To get needed nutrients, we should eat a variety of foods.	✓	○
3. Dairy products help grow strong bones.	✓	○

After You Read Lesson 5

Reread each statement above. If the lesson supports your choice, place a check mark in the *Correct* circle. Then explain how the text supports your choice. If the lesson does not support your choice, place a check mark in the *Incorrect* circle. Then explain why your choice is wrong.

	Correct	Incorrect
1. _____	○	○
2. _____	○	○
3. _____	○	○

Notes for Home: Your child has completed a pre/post inventory of key concepts in the lesson.
Home Activity: Plan a healthful lunch with your child. Together prepare the meal. Enjoy your lunch as you discuss the importance of eating a variety of foods.

Workbook   Think, Read, Learn **40**

Reviewing Concepts: True or False

Write **T** (True) or **F** (False) on the line before each statement.

T 1. People need food to survive.

F 2. Not all people need water.

T 3. People need to live in a clean environment.

T 4. Shelter helps people stay at a comfortable temperature.

F 5. Only people in cities need air to live.

T 6. Eating a variety of foods helps people stay healthy.

T 7. People who handle food should have clean hands.

F 8. The digestive system takes in the air people need to live.

Applying Strategies: Sequencing

Use complete sentences to answer question 9. (2 points)

9. The steps of what happens to food in the digestive system are shown out of order. Using the clue words in the sentences, write the steps in the correct order.

   Next, food is mixed with digestive juices in the stomach.
   Finally, solid waste is formed in the large intestine.
   First, the teeth break food into pieces.
   Then food particles pass into the bloodstream through the small intestine walls.

   First, the teeth break food into pieces. Next, food is mixed with digestive juices in the stomach. Then food particles pass into the bloodstream through the small intestine walls. Finally, solid waste is formed in the large intestine.

40A Lesson Review   Workbook

Workbook   Answer Key **T13**

Lesson 6: How can people stay healthy?

Before You Read Lesson 6

Read each statement below. Place a check mark in the circle to indicate whether you agree or disagree with the statement.

	Agree	Disagree
1. Exercise helps the heart, lungs, and muscles.	✔	○
2. Your lungs are part of your circulatory system.	○	✔
3. Bacteria and viruses are germs.	✔	○

After You Read Lesson 6

Reread each statement above. If the lesson supports your choice, place a check mark in the *Correct* circle. Then explain how the text supports your choice. If the lesson does not support your choice, place a check mark in the *Incorrect* circle. Then explain why your choice is wrong.

	Correct	Incorrect
1. _____	○	○
2. _____	○	○
3. _____	○	○

Notes for Home: Your child has completed a pre/post inventory of key concepts in the lesson.
Home Activity: Talk with your child about a time he or she became ill. Discuss how it happened and what you did to help your child get better.

Reviewing Terms: Matching

Match each description with the correct word or phrase. Write the letter on the line next to each description.

__b__ 1. very small living things or particles that can cause disease

__a__ 2. conditions in which parts of the body do not work properly

a. diseases
b. germs

Reviewing Concepts: Sentence Completion

Complete each sentence with the correct word.

__exercise__ 3. Sports and yard work are good ways to get _____. (exercise, rest)

__respiratory__ 4. Lungs are a part of the _____ system. (respiratory, circulatory)

__circulatory__ 5. The heart is a part of the _____ system. (digestive, circulatory)

__lungs__ 6. The windpipe is a tube that leads to the _____. (heart, lungs)

__germs__ 7. Flu and chicken pox are caused by _____. (germs, exercise)

__healthy__ 8. Exercise and rest can help people stay _____. (sick, healthy)

Applying Strategies: Converting

9. For one week, Tara's family recorded the number of hours and minutes they exercised. By the end of the week, Tara had exercised for 2 hours and 25 minutes. Show the amount of time that Tara exercised in minutes. Remember, 60 minutes are equal to 1 hour. Show your work. (2 points)

2 hours × 60 = 120 minutes + 25 minutes = 145 minutes total

Health by the Numbers

Read the cereal labels. Then answer the questions.

Tasty Squares
Serving Size: 1 cup
Calories: 170
Total Fat: 2.0 grams
Cholesterol: 0 grams
Sodium: 180 milligrams
Carbohydrates: 39 grams
Fiber: 3 grams
Sugar: 15 grams

Oaty Bits
Serving Size: 1 cup
Calories: 150
Total Fat: 1.0 grams
Cholesterol: 0 grams
Sodium: 95 milligrams
Carbohydrates: 25 grams
Fiber: 10 grams
Sugar: 11 grams

1. Jeb had two servings of Tasty Squares. How many calories did he eat? **340 calories**

2. Pauline had three servings of Oaty Bits. How much sodium did she eat? **285 milligrams**

3. How many more grams of carbohydrates are in a serving of Tasty Squares than in a serving of Oaty Bits?
   14 more grams

4. You should get 25 grams of fiber a day. How many servings of each cereal would it take to get 25 grams of fiber?
   Tasty Squares $8\frac{1}{3}$ **servings**
   Oaty Bits $2\frac{1}{2}$ **servings**

Notes for Home: Your child learned to read labels, compare their data, and solve problems based on the data.
Home Activity: Together compare the labels of several cereals your child eats. Rank them according to the amount of sugar, and then the amount of fiber.

Use the vocabulary words in the box to complete the labels on the diagram.

condensation
wetlands
evaporation
water vapor
precipitation
water cycle
groundwater

Water on Earth moves through a **water cycle** _____.

The Sun can turn water into a gas through **evaporation** _____.

Condensation happens when the gas cools to form water drops.

This gas, called **water vapor** _____, is in the air.

These drops of water may fall from clouds as **precipitation** _____.

Water is found in oceans, lakes, rivers, and **wetlands** _____ on Earth's surface.

Some water is stored inside the Earth as **groundwater** _____.

Notes for Home: Your child learned the vocabulary terms for Chapter 5.
Home Activity: Use vocabulary words as you talk with your child about how water changes form. Show evaporation and condensation using boiling water and a glass of ice water.

Cause and Effect

Read the science article.

What Happens to Rain?

What happens to the rain that falls? Some of it sinks into the ground. Some of it runs off into rivers and streams. And some of it rests in puddles. Over time, warmth from the Sun strikes water in puddles, causing it to evaporate. This water then becomes water vapor in the air.

Water vapor rises in the atmosphere. The higher it goes, the cooler the air becomes. When the water vapor becomes cool enough, it condenses. This means it forms droplets of water.

© Pearson Education, Inc.

Apply It!

Write the cause or causes for each effect in the boxes.

Cause(s)	Effect(s)
Warmth from Sun hits puddles.	1. Puddles evaporate. 2. Water vapor goes into air.
Water vapor rises.	Water droplets form.
It cools down as air gets cooler.	

Notes for Home: Your child learned how to identify causes and effects. **Home Activity:** Together read a newspaper or science magazine article that explains a process. Talk with your child about causes and effects the process explains.

© Pearson Education, Inc.

Lesson 1: Why is water important?

Before You Read Lesson 1

Read each statement below. Place a check mark in the circle to indicate whether you agree or disagree with the statement.

	Agree	Disagree
1. Your body is about two-thirds water.	✓	○
2. People use moving water to make electricity.	✓	○
3. Earth's surface is covered with groundwater.	○	✓

After You Read Lesson 1

Reread each statement above. If the lesson supports your choice, place a check mark in the *Correct* circle. Then explain how the text supports your choice. If the lesson does not support your choice, place a check mark in the *Incorrect* circle. Then explain why your choice is wrong.

	Correct	Incorrect
1. _____	○	○
_____		
2. _____	○	○
_____		
3. _____	○	○
_____		

Notes for Home: Your child has completed a pre/post inventory of key concepts in the lesson. **Home Activity:** Help your child chart how much water he or she drinks in a day. Encourage him or her to drink eight glasses a day.

© Pearson Education, Inc.

Reviewing Terms: Sentence Completion

Complete each sentence with the correct word or phrase.

water vapor 1. Water that is an invisible gas found in the air is called _____. (water vapor, groundwater)

wetland 2. A _____ is a place with wet or water-covered ground. (groundwater, wetland)

groundwater 3. Water that collects in spaces between underground rocks is called _____. (groundwater, ocean water)

Reviewing Concepts: True or False

Write **T** (True) or **F** (False) on the line before each statement.

T 4. Plants need water to make their own food.

F 5. Most animals can live without water.

T 6. The power of moving water can be used to make electricity.

F 7. Ocean water is used for drinking and washing clothes.

T 8. Many animals live in wetlands.

Writing

Use complete sentences to answer question 9. (2 points)

9. Describe one way that fresh water and ocean water are alike. Then describe one way they are different.

Sample answer: One similarity of ocean water and fresh water is that fish live in each type of water. A difference is that ocean water has a lot of salt in it and fresh water has only a little salt in it.

© Pearson Education, Inc.

Workbook

Answer Key **T15**

Lesson 2: How do forms of water change?

Before You Read Lesson 2

Read each statement below. Place a check mark in the circle to indicate whether you agree or disagree with the statement.

	Agree	Disagree
1. The water cycle gives us a supply of fresh water.	✓	○
2. At 32 degrees Fahrenheit, water becomes a gas.	○	✓
3. Water becomes a gas by evaporation.	✓	○

After You Read Lesson 2

Reread each statement above. If the lesson supports your choice, place a check mark in the *Correct* circle. Then explain how the text supports your choice. If the lesson does not support your choice, place a check mark in the *Incorrect* circle. Then explain why your choice is wrong.

	Correct	Incorrect
1. _____	○	○
_____		
2. _____	○	○
_____		
3. _____	○	○
_____		

Notes for Home: Your child has completed a pre/post inventory of key concepts in the lesson.
Home Activity: Talk about a rainstorm you and your child have experienced. Discuss how the rain formed and how water evaporated from puddles.

Workbook   Think, Read, Learn **49**

Reviewing Terms: Matching

Match each definition with the correct word or phrase. Write the letter on the line next to each definition.

b 1. movement of water back and forth between air and the Earth's surface

d 2. rain, snow, and sleet

a 3. water vapor changing to a liquid

c 4. liquid water becoming a gas

a. condensation
b. water cycle
c. evaporation
d. precipitation

Reviewing Concepts: Sentence Completion

Complete each sentence with the correct word.

Condensation 5. _____ is the process that causes dew to form. (Evaporation, Condensation)

wind 6. The Sun's energy and _____ cause evaporation as water moves through the water cycle. (wind, sleet)

temperature 7. The form of precipitation depends on the _____ at the Earth's surface. (condensation, temperature)

salt 8. Dirt, germs, and _____ are removed from water at a water-treatment plant. (fluoride, salt)

Applying Strategies: Identifying Cause and Effect

Use complete sentences to answer question 9. (2 points)

9. If the water in a lake is liquid, identify what must happen to the temperature to cause the water to become ice.

In order for the water to become ice, the temperature must decrease.

49A Lesson Review   Workbook

Symmetry and Shapes

Some shapes have symmetry. They are exactly the same on both sides of a line of symmetry. A symmetrical shape may have one, two, or more lines of symmetry.

Look at the figures. Use them to answer the questions.

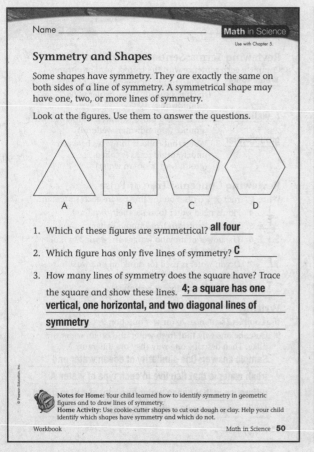

A   B   C   D

1. Which of these figures are symmetrical? **all four**

2. Which figure has only five lines of symmetry? **C**

3. How many lines of symmetry does the square have? Trace the square and show these lines. **4; a square has one vertical, one horizontal, and two diagonal lines of symmetry**

Notes for Home: Your child learned how to identify symmetry in geometric figures and to draw lines of symmetry.
Home Activity: Use cookie-cutter shapes to cut out dough or clay. Help your child identify which shapes have symmetry and which do not.

Workbook   Math in Science **50**

Use the vocabulary words in the box to complete the labels on the diagram. Use your own words to add more examples.

weather	hurricane	tornado	blizzard

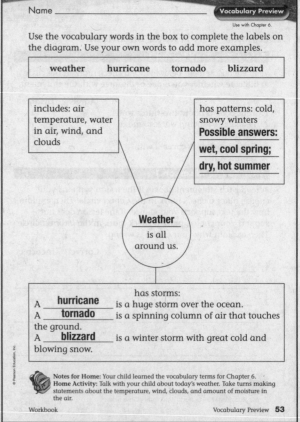

includes: air temperature, water in air, wind, and clouds

has patterns: cold, snowy winters
Possible answers: wet, cool spring; dry, hot summer

Weather is all around us.

has storms:
A **hurricane** is a huge storm over the ocean.
A **tornado** is a spinning column of air that touches the ground.
A **blizzard** is a winter storm with great cold and blowing snow.

Notes for Home: Your child learned the vocabulary terms for Chapter 6.
Home Activity: Talk with your child about today's weather. Take turns making statements about the temperature, wind, clouds, and amount of moisture in the air.

Workbook   Vocabulary Preview **53**

Make Inferences

Read the paragraph.

Hurricane Warning

The weather forecasters put out a hurricane warning for the Gulf Coast of Florida. The hurricane would hit land in two days. People were busy nailing wood over their windows. They bought extra food and water. Some people got in their cars and drove inland.

Apply It!

What inference can you make from the facts in the paragraph? Write the facts and your inference in the graphic organizer on page 55.

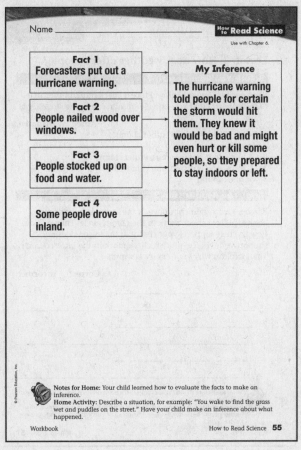

Fact 1 Forecasters put out a hurricane warning.	**My Inference** The hurricane warning told people for certain the storm would hit them. They knew it would be bad and might even hurt or kill some people, so they prepared to stay indoors or left.
Fact 2 People nailed wood over windows.	
Fact 3 People stocked up on food and water.	
Fact 4 Some people drove inland.	

Notes for Home: Your child learned how to evaluate the facts to make an inference.
Home Activity: Describe a situation, for example: "You wake to find the grass wet and puddles on the street." Have your child make an inference about what happened.

Lesson 1: What makes up weather?

Before You Read Lesson 1

Read each statement below. Place a check mark in the circle to indicate whether you agree or disagree with the statement.

	Agree	Disagree
1. Atmosphere is the blanket of gases around the Earth.	✓	○
2. A barometer measures wind speed.	○	✓
3. Air pressure is low when the air presses down a lot.	○	✓

After You Read Lesson 1

Reread each statement above. If the lesson supports your choice, place a check mark in the *Correct* circle. Then explain how the text supports your choice. If the lesson does not support your choice, place a check mark in the *Incorrect* circle. Then explain why your choice is wrong.

	Correct	Incorrect
1. _____	○	○
_____		
2. _____	○	○
_____		
3. _____	○	○

Notes for Home: Your child has completed a pre-/post-inventory of key concepts in the lesson.
Home Activity: Together watch or read a weather forecast. Talk with your child about a weather pattern that has occurred this week, such as a thunderstorm followed by clear, dry air.

Reviewing Terms: Sentence Completion

Complete each sentence with the correct word.

atmosphere 1. The blanket of air that surrounds Earth is the _____. (anemometer, atmosphere)

Weather 2. _____ is the temperature, clouds, precipitation, and wind conditions in an area. (Weather, Pollution)

Reviewing Concepts: True or False

Write **T** (True) or **F** (False) on the line before each statement.

T 3. Clouds are made up of water droplets in the air.

F 4. There is one kind of cloud.

T 5. Earth's atmosphere has layers that have different temperatures than one another.

T 6. The force of the atmosphere pressing down is called air pressure.

T 7. Humidity is the amount of water vapor in the air.

T 8. Weather data can be gathered with satellites.

Applying Strategies: Making Inferences

Use complete sentences to answer question 9. (2 points)

9. Terry checked the barometer reading several times during the day. The barometer reading was lower each time she checked. What does a barometer measure? What weather conditions could Terry expect?

A barometer measures air pressure. Terry should expect cloudy or rainy weather.

Name _____

Think, Read, Learn
Use with pages 180–183.

Lesson 2: How does weather affect people?

Before You Read Lesson 2

Read each statement below. Place a check mark in the circle to indicate whether you agree or disagree with the statement.

	Agree	Disagree
1. In most places, the weather changes in a pattern.	☑	○
2. A blizzard is a dangerous winter storm.	☑	○
3. A hurricane is a spinning cloud on the ground.	○	☑

After You Read Lesson 2

Reread each statement above. If the lesson supports your choice, place a check mark in the *Correct* circle. Then explain how the text supports your choice. If the lesson does not support your choice, place a check mark in the *Incorrect* circle. Then explain why your choice is wrong.

	Correct	Incorrect
1. _____ _____	○	○
2. _____ _____	○	○
3. _____	○	○

Notes for Home: Your child has completed a pre-/post-inventory of key concepts in the lesson.
Home Activity: Talk with your child about a storm that can occur in your area (thunderstorm, hurricane, tornado, blizzard). List safety tips and ways to prepare for the storm.

Workbook   Think, Read, Learn **57**

Name _____

Lesson 2 Review
Use with pages 180–183.

Reviewing Terms: Matching

Match each definition with the correct word. Write the letter on the line next to each definition.

__b__ 1. a winter storm with blowing snow

__c__ 2. a storm with a funnel-shaped column of air that touches the ground

__a__ 3. storms with heavy rain, strong winds, and huge waves

a. hurricane
b. blizzard
c. tornado

Reviewing Concepts: Sentence Completion

Complete the sentence with the correct word or phrase.

__different__ 4. Patterns of weather are _____ everywhere on Earth. (different, the same)

__colder__ 5. As air moves up a mountain it gets _____. (colder, wetter)

__dry__ 6. All deserts are _____. (hot, dry)

__floods__ 7. Heavy rains and very high waves can both cause _____. (floods, blizzards)

__wind__ 8. Hurricanes, tornados, and blizzards all have _____. (wind, low temperatures)

Writing

Use a complete sentence to answer question 9. (2 points)

9. Write a sentence that describes one way the National Weather Service helps to keep people safe.

Sample answer: The National Weather Service helps people to stay safe during storms by putting out storm watches and warnings.

57A Lesson Review   Workbook

Name _____

Math in Science
Use with Chapter 6.

Comparing Temperatures

The table shows temperatures for the town of Smithport. Each temperature represents the average daytime high for July in a certain year. Do you see a pattern?

Changes in High Temperature for Smithport, 1980–2005

Year	1980	1985	1990	1995	2000	2005
Average daytime high for July	79°	79°	81°	80°	83°	84°

Use the table to answer these questions.

1. What trend, or pattern, do you see happening over 25 years?
   The average daytime high temperature increased.

2. When did the biggest change occur?
   from 1995 to 2000

3. How much warmer was it, on average, in July in Smithport in 2000 than in 1985?
   4 degrees warmer

4. What could explain the change?
   Possible answers: The pattern of weather is becoming warmer overall. Something changed in the town's environment, such as more factories and buildings and fewer trees.

Notes for Home: Your child learned how to read a table to compare data.
Home Activity: Help your child make a table showing the high temperature every day for a week. Talk about any pattern you see.

Workbook   Math in Science **58**

Name _____

Vocabulary Preview
Use with Chapter 7.

Read the clues. Choose a word to answer each riddle.

rock	metamorphic rock	igneous rock
mineral	sedimentary rock	decay
soil	nutrient	loam

1. Granite is an example. It forms deep underground. It needs heat to form. What is it? **igneous rock**

2. When they die, plants and animals do this. It means to break down into bits. What is it? **decay**

3. It covers most of the land on Earth. It is made up of bits of rock and dead plant and animal matter. It is a home to earthworms. What is it? **soil**

4. It is a natural material. It has never been living. Every rock contains at least one. What is it? **mineral**

5. Heat and pressure made it what it is today. Its name means "changes form." Slate is an example. What is it? **metamorphic rock**

6. It is a kind of soil. Plants grow well in it. It holds lots of water. It is a mixture. What is it? **loam**

7. It forms in layers. It might contain fossils. It can tell a "story" about how life has changed over time. What is it? **sedimentary rock**

8. A mountain is mostly this. It is solid and nonliving. It contains one or more minerals. It can be placed in one of three main groups. What is it? **rock**

9. It is a material that plants take from soil. It helps plants grow. It might come from a mineral or decaying plants and animals. What is it? **nutrient**

Notes for Home: Your child learned the vocabulary terms for Chapter 7.
Home Activity: Have your child cut out magazine pictures or draw pictures that illustrate the vocabulary words. Make up sentences together that use the words.

Workbook   Vocabulary Preview **61**

Compare and Contrast

Read the magazine article and look at the pictures. How are rocks and soil alike and different?

Rocks and Soil

The solid surface of Earth is covered with rocks and soil. Rocks are made of one or more minerals. Minerals are natural nonliving materials. Rocks may be large or small, but they are solid and hard to break. When rocks break down, soil can start to form. Soil is a loose mix of tiny bits of rock and material from dead plants and animals. Water will soak up into soil, but it runs off of rock.

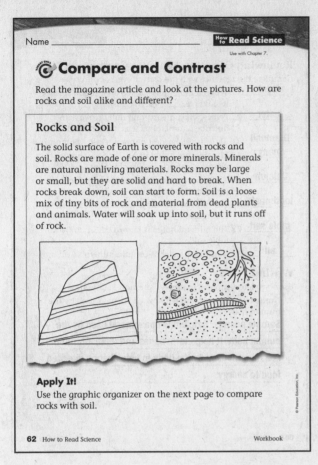

Apply It!
Use the graphic organizer on the next page to compare rocks with soil.

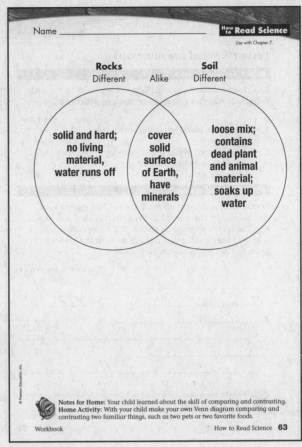

Rocks
Different   Alike   Soil
Different

solid and hard; no living material, water runs off

cover solid surface of Earth, have minerals

loose mix; contains dead plant and animal material; soaks up water

Notes for Home: Your child learned about the skill of comparing and contrasting.
Home Activity: With your child make your own Venn diagram comparing and contrasting two familiar things, such as two pets or two favorite foods.

Lesson 1: How do rocks form?

Before You Read Lesson 1

Read each statement below. Place a check mark in the circle to indicate whether you agree or disagree with the statement.

	Agree	Disagree
1. Rocks are made of one or more minerals.	✓	○
2. Igneous rock forms in layers.	○	✓
3. Fossils are usually found in metamorphic rock.	○	✓

After You Read Lesson 1

Reread each statement above. If the lesson supports your choice, place a check mark in the *Correct* circle. Then explain how the text supports your choice. If the lesson does not support your choice, place a check mark in the *Incorrect* circle. Then explain why your choice is wrong.

	Correct	Incorrect
1. _____	○	○
2. _____	○	○
3. _____	○	○

Notes for Home: Your child has completed a pre/post inventory of key concepts in the lesson.
Home Activity: Gather stones and sort them into groups according to similarities. Use the words *color*, *texture*, and *minerals* to describe the rock groups.

Reviewing Terms: Matching

Match each description with the correct word or phrase. Write the letter on the line next to each description.

__c__ 1. any solid, nonliving material made of one or more mineral

__d__ 2. a natural material that forms from nonliving matter

__b__ 3. a rock that forms from a mixture of melted material and gases

__a__ 4. a rock made of layers that are cemented together

__e__ 5. a rock that has been changed by heat and pressure

a. sedimentary rock
b. igneous rock
c. rock
d. mineral
e. metamorphic rock

Reviewing Concepts: True or False

Write **T** (True) or **F** (False) on the line before each statement.

__F__ 6. All rocks have the same texture and grain size.

__F__ 7. Fossils are most often found in metamorphic rock.

__T__ 8. Igneous rock can come from volcanoes.

Applying Concepts: Compare and Contrast

Use complete sentences to answer question 9. (2 points)

9. Name one way in which sedimentary, igneous, and metamorphic rocks are similar and one way in which they are different.

Sample answer: All three types of rocks are made up of solid, nonliving materials and contain one or more minerals. The three kinds of rock differ in the way that they are formed.

Lesson 2: What are minerals?

Before You Read Lesson 2

Read each statement below. Place a check mark in the circle to indicate whether you agree or disagree with the statement.

	Agree	Disagree
1. Minerals are identified using only their color.	○	✔
2. You have used several minerals today.	✔	○
3. Most foods except for vegetables contain minerals.	○	✔

After You Read Lesson 2

Reread each statement above. If the lesson supports your choice, place a check mark in the *Correct* circle. Then explain how the text supports your choice. If the lesson does not support your choice, place a check mark in the *Incorrect* circle. Then explain why your choice is wrong.

	Correct	Incorrect
1. _____	○	○
2. _____	○	○
3. _____	○	○

Notes for Home: Your child has completed a pre/post inventory of key concepts in the lesson.
Home Activity: List some minerals, such as copper, quartz, graphite, and iron. Go on a household search for products that contain one or more of these minerals.

Reviewing Concepts: Sentence Completion

Complete the sentence with the correct word or phrase.

streak 1. When a mineral is rubbed on a rough surface, it leaves a _____. (streak, luster)

luster 2. Pearly, silky, greasy, and dull are ways to describe a mineral's _____. (luster, hardness)

Diamond 3. _____ is the hardest mineral. (Talc, Diamond)

many 4. Minerals are found in _____ of the things people use every day. (many, few)

Calcium 5. _____ is a mineral that helps bones form. (Copper, Calcium)

toothpaste 6. The mineral fluorite is found in _____. (steel, toothpaste)

table salt 7. The mineral halite is known as _____. (lead, table salt)

all 8. Almost _____ foods contain minerals. (all, no)

Writing

Use complete sentences to answer question 9. (2 points)

9. Name two minerals and tell how each one is used by the human body.

Sample answer: Calcium is one mineral used by the human body. It helps form bones and teeth. Chromium is a mineral used by the body to help change digested food to energy.

Lesson 3: Why is soil important?

Before You Read Lesson 3

Read each statement below. Place a check mark in the circle to indicate whether you agree or disagree with the statement.

	Agree	Disagree
1. Soil is made of decaying plants and animals.	○	✔
2. The top layer of soil is called topsoil.	✔	○
3. Good soil does not contain living things.	○	✔

After You Read Lesson 3

Reread each statement above. If the lesson supports your choice, place a check mark in the *Correct* circle. Then explain how the text supports your choice. If the lesson does not support your choice, place a check mark in the *Incorrect* circle. Then explain why your choice is wrong.

	Correct	Incorrect
1. _____	○	○
2. _____	○	○
3. _____	○	○

Notes for Home: Your child has completed a pre/post inventory of key concepts in the lesson.
Home Activity: Put sand and potting soil into plastic cups. Compare how much water each can hold. Draw a conclusion about which is better for plants.

Reviewing Terms: Matching

Match each description with the correct word. Write the letter on the line next to each description.

c 1. a thin layer of loose material that covers Earth's land
d 2. the process of breaking down the remains of plants and animals
b 3. a kind of material released by decay
a 4. a soil with a mixture of sand, silt, clay, and humus

a. loam
b. nutrient
c. soil
d. decay

Reviewing Concepts: True or False

Write **T** (True) or **F** (False) on the line before each statement.

F 5. It takes about ten years for nature to rebuild lost topsoil.
F 6. Topsoil is the bottom layer of soil.
T 7. Clay has the smallest soil particle size.
T 8. Loam is soil that is good for growing plants.

Applying Concepts: Calculating

9. In a certain area the topsoil is 1.5 meters deep, the subsoil is 3.0 meters deep, and the bedrock is 6.0 meters deep. How many meters deep are all three soil layers together? Show your work. (2 points)

1.5 m + 3.0 m + 6.0 m = 10.5 m.

Minerals in Foods

Look at the table. A group of students looked at labels on food products at home. They recorded the number of foods they found that contain each mineral on the label.

Mineral	Calcium	Iron	Sodium	Potassium	Copper
Number of foods that have this mineral	32	24	51	12	8

Use the table to answer the questions.

1. Which mineral was found in the most foods?

   sodium

2. Which mineral was found in the fewest foods?

   copper

3. The students looked at a total of 60 foods. How many foods in their sample were sodium free?

   9

4. Which mineral was found in twice as many foods as potassium was found?

   iron

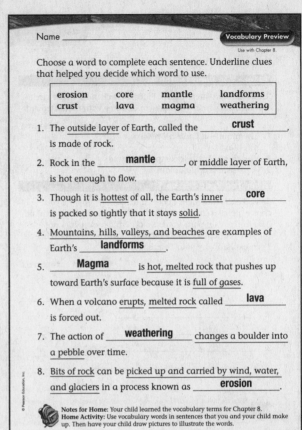

Notes for Home: Your child learned to read a table to compare data.
Home Activity: Help your child make a table showing how much calcium is in different dairy products. Compare which gives the most and least calcium per serving.

Choose a word to complete each sentence. Underline clues that helped you decide which word to use.

erosion	core	mantle	landforms
crust	lava	magma	weathering

1. The outside layer of Earth, called the _____**crust**_____, is made of rock.

2. Rock in the _____**mantle**_____, or middle layer of Earth, is hot enough to flow.

3. Though it is hottest of all, the Earth's inner _____**core**_____ is packed so tightly that it stays solid.

4. Mountains, hills, valleys, and beaches are examples of Earth's _____**landforms**_____.

5. _____**Magma**_____ is hot, melted rock that pushes up toward Earth's surface because it is full of gases.

6. When a volcano erupts, melted rock called _____**lava**_____ is forced out.

7. The action of _____**weathering**_____ changes a boulder into a pebble over time.

8. Bits of rock can be picked up and carried by wind, water, and glaciers in a process known as _____**erosion**_____.

Notes for Home: Your child learned the vocabulary terms for Chapter 8.
Home Activity: Use vocabulary words in sentences that you and your child make up. Then have your child draw pictures to illustrate the words.

Sequence

Read the science article.

Growing a Glacier

It takes many years to grow a glacier. First, in a very cold place, snow keeps piling up because it does not melt from year to year. Then top layers press down on lower layers, packing them together. Next, the weight changes bottom layers of snow into ice. Finally, the force is so great it causes the glacier to move over the ground, scraping rocks and dirt as it goes.

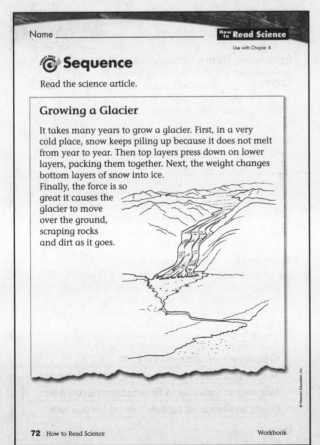

Apply It!
How does a glacier form? Write the steps in order on the graphic organizer.

First
Snowfall piles on snowfall.

↓

Next
Lower layers are packed down.

↓

Then
Lower layers turn into ice.

↓

Finally
Huge forces pressing down cause the glacier to move over the ground.

Notes for Home: Your child learned how to sequence events.
Home Activity: Have your child draw a sequence chart showing how forces press on a glacier and cause it to move.

Workbook   Answer Key **T21**

Use with pages 223–225.

Lesson 1: What are Earth's layers?

Before You Read Lesson 1

Read each statement below. Place a check mark in the circle to indicate whether you agree or disagree with the statement.

	Agree	Disagree
1. The mantle of Earth moves like soft plastic.	✓	○
2. The core of Earth is completely liquid.	○	✓
3. A plateau is a high plain.	✓	○

After You Read Lesson 1

Reread each statement above. If the lesson supports your choice, place a check mark in the *Correct* circle. Then explain how the text supports your choice. If the lesson does not support your choice, place a check mark in the *Incorrect* circle. Then explain why your choice is wrong.

	Correct	Incorrect
1. _____	○	○
2. _____	○	○
3. _____	○	○

Notes for Home: Your child has completed a pre/post inventory of key concepts in the lesson.
Home Activity: Take a walking tour or look at pictures of local landforms with your child. Discuss how these features might have been shaped by nature.

Workbook   Think, Read, Learn **74**

Use with pages 223–225.

Reviewing Terms: Sentence Completion

Complete each sentence with the correct word.

__crust__ 1. The _____ is the outer layer of Earth. (crust, core)

__mantle__ 2. Earth's middle layer is the _____. (core, mantle)

__core__ 3. The innermost layer of the Earth is the _____. (crust, core)

__Landforms__ 4. _____ are solid features on Earth's crust. (Oceans, Landforms)

Reviewing Concepts: Matching

Match each landform with the correct description. Write the letter on the line next to each description.

__b__ 5. a large, mostly flat area   a. valley
__c__ 6. the land next to the ocean   b. plain
__a__ 7. a low, narrow area   c. coast
__d__ 8. a high place   d. hill

Writing

Use complete sentences to answer question 9. (2 points)

9. Write a short paragraph that describes Earth's layers.

Sample answer: Earth is made of three layers. The outer layer is the crust, which is made of hard rock. The middle layer is the mantle. The mantle is made of hot, slowly flowing rock. The core is the innermost layer of Earth. The core is made of metal.

74A Lesson Review   Workbook

Use with pages 226–229.

Lesson 2: What are volcanoes and earthquakes?

Before You Read Lesson 2

Read each statement below. Place a check mark in the circle to indicate whether you agree or disagree with the statement.

	Agree	Disagree
1. Lava hardens to form igneous rock.	✓	○
2. Moving parts of Earth's crust cause earthquakes.	✓	○
3. Earthquakes often happen along faults.	✓	○

After You Read Lesson 2

Reread each statement above. If the lesson supports your choice, place a check mark in the *Correct* circle. Then explain how the text supports your choice. If the lesson does not support your choice, place a check mark in the *Incorrect* circle. Then explain why your choice is wrong.

	Correct	Incorrect
1. _____	○	○
2. _____	○	○
3. _____	○	○

Notes for Home: Your child has completed a pre/post inventory of key concepts in the lesson.
Home Activity: Ask your child to explain how earthquakes and volcanoes are related to the crust and mantle of Earth.

Workbook   Think, Read, Learn **75**

Use with pages 226–229.

Reviewing Terms: Sentence Completion

Complete each sentence with the correct word.

__Magma__ 1. _____ is hot, melted rock under the ground. (Lava, Magma)

__lava__ 2. Melted rock that has come out of a volcano is called _____. (lava, eruption)

Reviewing Concepts: True or False

Write T (True) or F (False) on the line before each statement.

__F__ 3. Magma forms in Earth's core.
__T__ 4. A volcano is an opening in Earth's crust.
__F__ 5. When lava cools, it becomes sedimentary rock.
__T__ 6. Magma collects underground in magma chambers.
__T__ 7. Earthquake vibrations travel as waves.
__F__ 8. The farther an earthquake is from a city, the more damage it causes there.

Applying Strategies: Sequence

Use complete sentences to answer question 9. (2 points)

9. Using the clue words in the sentences, write the steps of a volcanic eruption in the correct order.

Next, magma pushes up through cracks in Earth's crust.
First, magma forms deep in the Earth.
Finally, lava cools and hardens, forming igneous rock.
Then magma comes out of the volcano and is called lava.

First, magma forms deep in the Earth.

Next, magma pushes up through cracks in Earth's crust.

Then magma comes out of the volcano and is called lava.

Finally, lava cools and hardens, forming igneous rock.

75A Lesson Review   Workbook

© Pearson Education, Inc.

Use with pages 230–233.

Lesson 3: What are weathering and erosion?

Before You Read Lesson 3

Read each statement below. Place a check mark in the circle to indicate whether you agree or disagree with the statement.

	Agree	Disagree
1. Erosion is caused mostly by wind.	○	✓
2. Weathering causes rocks to break up.	✓	○
3. Living things do not cause weathering.	○	✓

After You Read Lesson 3

Reread each statement above. If the lesson supports your choice, place a check mark in the *Correct* circle. Then explain how the text supports your choice. If the lesson does not support your choice, place a check mark in the *Incorrect* circle. Then explain why your choice is wrong.

	Correct	Incorrect
1. _____	○	○
2. _____	○	○
3. _____	○	○

Notes for Home: Your child has completed a pre/post inventory of key concepts in the lesson.
Home Activity: Freeze an exact amount of water in a measuring cup and then remeasure it. Talk about how the increase in the volume of water when it freezes helps break up rocks.

Use with pages 230–233.

Reviewing Terms: Matching

Match each description with the correct word. Write the letter on the line next to each description.

__b__ 1. any action that breaks rocks into smaller pieces

__a__ 2. the movement of broken rocks and Earth materials

a. erosion
b. weathering

Reviewing Concepts: Sentence Completion

Complete the sentence with the correct word or phrase.

__always__ 3. Landforms _____ change. (always, never)

__weathering__ 4. Plant's roots can cause _____. (weathering, erosion)

__Freezing__ 5. _____ makes water expand and crack rocks. (Freezing, Thawing)

__erosion__ 6. Rainwater causes soil loss by _____. (erosion, gravity)

__wind__ 7. In dry areas like deserts, _____ causes most of the erosion. (wind, water)

__gravity__ 8. A mudflow is caused by _____. (wind, gravity)

Applying Concepts: Comparing Numbers

9. Using the list below, tell what kind of rock is 10 times larger than a pebble. Explain how you know. (2 points)

Sizes of Rocks

Boulder	300 mm	Cobble	100 mm
Pebble	30 mm	Sand	1 mm

I know that a boulder is 10 times larger than a pebble because 30 mm × 10 = 300 mm (the size of a boulder).

Use with Chapter 8.

Measuring an Earthquake

The Richter scale measures the strength of earthquakes. Very weak earthquakes have a number from 1 to 3. The strongest earthquakes measure 7 or 8 on the Richter scale.

Richter Magnitude	Effects	Number
Less than 2.0	Not felt	About 8,000 per day
2.0–2.9	Usually not felt	About 1,000 per day
3.0–3.9	Often felt, but rarely causes damage	49,000 per year
4.0–4.9	Not much damage likely	6,200 per year
5.0–5.9	Damage to poorly made buildings over a small area	800 per year
6.0–6.9	Property destroyed over an area up to 100 miles across	120 per year
7.0–7.9	Serious damage over a larger area	18 per year
8.0 or greater	Serious damage in areas several hundred miles across	1 per year

Use the table to answer the questions.

1. About how many earthquakes with a magnitude of 5.0 to 5.9 occur each year? **800**

2. What effects can an earthquake with a magnitude of 6.0 to 6.9 have? **It can destroy property over an area up to 100 miles across.**

3. How would you describe the relationship of the size, or magnitude, of earthquakes and the number of earthquakes that occur each year? **The weaker the earthquake, the more there are. Very few really strong earthquakes occur each year.**

Notes for Home: Your child learned how earthquake size and strength are measured.
Home Activity: Talk with your child about any earthquakes in your area. Visit a library or Web site to learn about what to do for safety during an earthquake.

Use with Chapter 9.

Circle the letter of the answer that best completes the meaning of the boldfaced word.

1. **Natural resources** are materials from the Earth that living things need, such as ___.
   A. air
   B. water
   C. minerals
   D. all of the above

2. Some resources are **renewable**, which means that they ___.
   A. can be replaced
   B. cannot be replaced
   C. are not needed
   D. are needed more than other resources

3. **Nonrenewable resources**, such as oil, coal, and iron, must be used carefully because ___.
   A. they are dangerous
   B. we have very little of these resources
   C. Earth cannot replace them
   D. they pollute the Earth

4. **Conservation** will help people in the long run because it ___.
   A. helps us find new resources
   B. prevents the waste of resources
   C. purifies dirty water
   D. blows away soil

5. To **recycle** resources, you must ___.
   A. change them so they can be used again
   B. use them over and over
   C. throw them away
   D. use less of them

Notes for Home: Your child learned the vocabulary terms for Chapter 9.
Home Activity: Use vocabulary words as you and your child put away groceries and other items. Discuss the resources used to make these products and how you can conserve and recycle.

Compare and Contrast

Read the science article.

Energy

We burn a lot of coal to produce energy. In fact, coal furnishes 22 percent of the energy used in the United States. Mostly, coal energy is changed into electricity or used to run steam engines. However, burning coal releases pollution into the air. To get coal, we must mine it from the ground, which is dangerous for workers. Also, one day, we will run out of coal.

Solar energy is energy from the Sun. People capture it using panels or cells. These devices change the solar energy into heat energy or electric energy. This energy supply is clean and unlimited. However, it takes time to collect enough solar energy to use, and the devices used to collect it make it more expensive than other forms of energy. Also, clouds and night take away the source of this energy.

© Pearson Education, Inc.

Apply It!

Fill in the graphic organizer. Write how solar energy and energy from burning coal are alike and different.

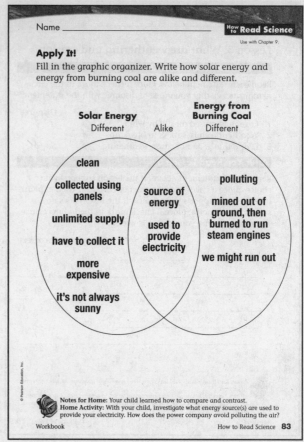

Solar Energy
Different

Alike

Energy from Burning Coal
Different

clean

collected using panels

unlimited supply

have to collect it

more expensive

it's not always sunny

source of energy

used to provide electricity

polluting

mined out of ground, then burned to run steam engines

we might run out

Notes for Home: Your child learned how to compare and contrast.
Home Activity: With your child, investigate what energy source(s) are used to provide your electricity. How does the power company avoid polluting the air?

Lesson 1: What are resources?

Before You Read Lesson 1

Read each statement below. Place a check mark in the circle to indicate whether you agree or disagree with the statement.

	Agree	Disagree
1. To renew the resource of trees, you plant new ones.	✓	○
2. Fuels such as oil, natural gas, and coal are renewable resources.	○	✓
3. Sunlight is a nonrenewable resource.	○	✓

After You Read Lesson 1

Reread each statement above. If the lesson supports your choice, place a check mark in the *Correct* circle. Then explain how the text supports your choice. If the lesson does not support your choice, place a check mark in the *Incorrect* circle. Then explain why your choice is wrong.

	Correct	Incorrect
1. _____	○	○
2. _____	○	○
3. _____	○	○

Notes for Home: Your child has completed a pre/post inventory of key concepts in the lesson.
Home Activity: With your child, go on a search to identify products and furnishings in your home that are made from trees, iron ore, oil, or coal.

Reviewing Terms: Matching

Match each description with the correct phrase. Write the letter on the line next to each description.

<u>b</u> 1. important materials from Earth that living things need

<u>a</u> 2. resources that can be replaced in a fairly short time

<u>c</u> 3. resources that cannot be replaced

a. renewable resources

b. natural resources

c. nonrenewable resources

Reviewing Concepts: True or False

Write **T** (True) or **F** (False) on the line before each statement.

<u>T</u> 4. Wood is a natural resource.

<u>F</u> 5. Trees are a nonrenewable resource.

<u>T</u> 6. Ores are rocks that contain metals or minerals.

<u>F</u> 7. Iron is a renewable resource.

<u>T</u> 8. Sunlight is a resource that cannot get used up.

Writing

Use complete sentences to answer question 9. (2 points)

9. Describe one natural resource and explain how it is used by people.

Sample answer: Coal is a nonrenewable natural resource. It is used by people for fuel. Energy from burning coal can be used to heat homes and businesses.

© Pearson Education, Inc.

T24 Answer Key

Workbook

Lesson 2: How can we protect our resources?

Before You Read Lesson 2

Read each statement below. Place a check mark in the circle to indicate whether you agree or disagree with the statement.

	Agree	Disagree
1. When you conserve resources, you waste them.	○	☑
2. Most of our trash is paper.	☑	○
3. Landfills are large areas where trash is buried.	☑	○

After You Read Lesson 2

Reread each statement above. If the lesson supports your choice, place a check mark in the *Correct* circle. Then explain how the text supports your choice. If the lesson does not support your choice, place a check mark in the *Incorrect* circle. Then explain why your choice is wrong.

	Correct	Incorrect
1. _____	○	○
2. _____	○	○
3. _____	○	○

Notes for Home: Your child has completed a pre/post inventory of key concepts in the lesson.
Home Activity: List ways you and your child could conserve resources such as fuels. For example, you might walk to school together rather than use a car.

Workbook **Think, Read, Learn 85**

Reviewing Terms: Sentence Completion

Complete the sentence with the correct word.

Conservation 1. _____ is the wise use of any natural resource. (Compost, Conservation)

Reviewing Concepts: Sentence Completion

Complete each sentence with the correct word.

less 2. You can conserve water by using _____ of it. (more, less)

clean 3. Wetlands can _____ water. (clean, compost)

erosion 4. Wind and water can cause soil _____. (conservation, erosion)

compost 5. Decay can turn yard clippings into _____. (water, compost)

landfill 6. A _____ is a place where trash is buried. (landfill, wetland)

cleaned 7. Smoke from burning garbage must be _____ before it is released into the air. (cleaned, conserved)

Less 8. _____ landfill space would be needed if people made smaller amounts of trash. (Less, More)

Applying Strategies: Compare and Contrast

Use complete sentences to answer question 9. (2 points)

9. What is one way that conserving soil and conserving water are similar actions? What is one way they are different?
Sample answer: The conservation of water and soil are both ways to care for the Earth. Conserving water can be done by using less water. Soil is conserved by protecting it from erosion.

85A Lesson Review Workbook

Lesson 3: What are ways to use resources again?

Before You Read Lesson 3

Read each statement below. Place a check mark in the circle to indicate whether you agree or disagree with the statement.

	Agree	Disagree
1. When you recycle something, you change it so that it can be used again.	☑	○
2. Glass can only be recycled once.	○	☑
3. The three *R*'s for protecting resources are *renewal, refuse,* and *resource.*	○	☑

After You Read Lesson 3

Reread each statement above. If the lesson supports your choice, place a check mark in the *Correct* circle. Then explain how the text supports your choice. If the lesson does not support your choice, place a check mark in the *Incorrect* circle. Then explain why your choice is wrong.

	Correct	Incorrect
1. _____	○	○
2. _____	○	○
3. _____	○	○

Notes for Home: Your child has completed a pre/post inventory of key concepts in the lesson.
Home Activity: Begin a family reuse program in which everyone tries to find ways to reuse things the family no longer needs or wants. For example, an old towel could be torn up for use as rags.

Workbook **Think, Read, Learn 86**

Reviewing Terms: Sentence Completion

Complete the sentence with the correct word.

recycle 1. To _____ is to make something into a new product so it can be used again. (reuse, recycle)

Reviewing Concepts: True or False

Write **T** (True) or **F** (False) on the line before each statement.

T 2. Reusing things is one way to conserve resources.

T 3. Metal, glass, paper, and plastic are materials that can be recycled.

F 4. In reusing, a new product is made.

F 5. Reusing things to conserve resources is a new idea.

F 6. Recycling glass does not save energy.

T 7. Buying products made from recycled materials helps conserve resources.

T 8. Reduce, reuse, and recycle are three ways to care for the Earth.

Applying Strategies: Calculating

9. People recycle 70 kilograms of cardboard for every 100 kilograms produced. If 500 kilograms of cardboard are produced, how many kilograms will be recycled? Show your work. (2 points)

70 kg/100 kg × 500 kg = 350 kg

86A Lesson Review Workbook

Workbook Answer Key **T25**

Disappearing Forests

The graph shows how much tropical forest has been lost in just 30 years in three regions of the world as well as in the world overall.

Percent of Tropical Forest Cleared
Between 1960 and 1990

Use the graph to answer these questions.

1. What percent of Asia's tropical forests was cut down between 1960 and 1990? **30 percent**

2. The bar for *World* shows the average percent of tropical forest cut down in all regions. What percent of the world's tropical forests was cut down between 1960 and 1990? **20 percent**

3. What conclusion can you draw from what this graph shows? **Possible answer: If this rate of cutting down tropical forests continues, the world will soon lose most of its tropical forests.**

Notes for Home: Your child learned to read a bar graph.
Home Activity: Together count the number of food cans, boxes, and packages in your kitchen and make a bar graph that shows this data. Then ask your child questions about the bar graph.

Circle the letter of the answer that best tells what the boldfaced word means.

1. Everything around you is made of **matter**—even the air.
   A. simple things
   Ⓑ anything that has mass and takes up space
2. Use your senses to discover the **properties** of a thing.
   A. true statements   Ⓑ qualities you can observe
3. As you blow up a balloon, air inside it has more and more **pressure.**
   Ⓐ pushing force   B. volume
4. The smallest particles of an **element** keep all the properties of the element.
   A. tiny piece
   Ⓑ substance made of one kind of particle
5. Gold is made up only of **atoms** of gold, but one **atom** of gold would be far too small to see.
   Ⓐ smallest unit of an element
   B. smallest particle possible
6. Every element has its place on the **periodic table.**
   A. list of matter   Ⓑ orderly arrangement of elements
7. You can measure an object's **mass** with a scale or a balance.
   Ⓐ amount of matter   B. size
8. When you measure milk for a cake, you measure its **volume.**
   A. weight   Ⓑ space taken up
9. Two balls of the same size that weigh different amounts have a different **density.**
   A. volume   Ⓑ amount of matter per unit of space
10. A plastic lid has more **buoyancy** than a rock.
    Ⓐ ability to float   B. ability to sink

Notes for Home: Your child learned the vocabulary terms for Chapter 10.
Home Activity: Have your child use pictures and other graphics in Chapter 10 to explain the meanings of the vocabulary words.

Ⓒ Cause and Effect

Read the science article.

How Ice Cream Melts

A solid can change into a liquid. For example, on a hot day ice cream melts quickly. What causes this to happen? The ice cream absorbs heat energy from the sun. This adds energy to the tiny particles of which the ice cream is made. Then the particles can move around more freely. As a result, the solid ice cream becomes a liquid that can be poured.

Apply It!

Fill in the graphic organizer. Write three causes and an effect from the article.

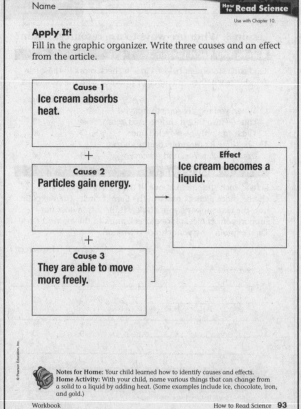

Cause 1
Ice cream absorbs heat.

+

Cause 2
Particles gain energy.

+

Cause 3
They are able to move more freely.

Effect
Ice cream becomes a liquid.

Notes for Home: Your child learned how to identify causes and effects.
Home Activity: With your child, name various things that can change from a solid to a liquid by adding heat. (Some examples include ice, chocolate, iron, and gold.)

T26   Answer Key   Workbook

Use with pages 279–283.

Lesson 1: How can we describe matter?

Before You Read Lesson 1

Read each statement below. Place a check mark in the circle to indicate whether you agree or disagree with the statement.

	Agree	Disagree
1. All matter is solid or liquid.	○	✓
2. The particles of a solid stay in place.	✓	○
3. In an element, all particles are one kind.	✓	○

After You Read Lesson 1

Reread each statement above. If the lesson supports your choice, place a check mark in the *Correct* circle. Then explain how the text supports your choice. If the lesson does not support your choice, place a check mark in the *Incorrect* circle. Then explain why your choice is wrong.

	Correct	Incorrect
1. _____	○	○
_____		
2. _____	○	○
_____		
3. _____	○	○
_____		

Notes for Home: Your child has completed a pre/post inventory of key concepts in the lesson.
Home Activity: Have your child choose a solid, a liquid, and a gas (air in a balloon) available at home. Demonstrate the properties of each kind of matter.

Use with pages 279–283.

Reviewing Terms: Matching

Match each description with the correct word or phrase. Write the letter on the line next to each description.

f   1. anything that takes up space and has weight
a   2. something you can observe about matter
c   3. pushing by particles in matter
d   4. matter made of a single type of particle
e   5. the smallest particle of an element that has the properties of the element
b   6. a way of arranging elements based on their properties

a. property
b. periodic table
c. pressure
d. element
e. atom
f. matter

Reviewing Concepts: Sentence Completion

Complete the sentence with the correct word.

solid 7. Matter that is a _____ does not change its shape. (solid, gas)

gas 8. A _____ expands and fills all the space available. (gas, liquid)

Writing

Use complete sentences to answer question 9. (2 points)

9. Describe one of the states of matter. Then give one example of something you use every day that is found in that state of matter.

Sample answer: A gas is a state of matter with particles that move freely. One gas that I use every day is air.

Use with Chapter 10.

Measuring and Comparing Properties

Use the pictures to answer the questions.

A   B   C

1. What property is being measured in drawings A and B?
   length

2. How much longer is the finger than the toe?
   2 cm longer

3. What property is being measured in drawing C?
   volume

4. How will this property change if the milk is poured into a glass? **It will not change.**

Notes for Home: Your child learned about measuring length and volume and comparing measurements.
Home Activity: Put water in a measuring cup and line up different-sized glasses. Have your child predict which ones will hold all the water. Check the predictions.

Use with pages 284–289.

Reviewing Terms: Sentence Completion

Complete each sentence with the correct word.

mass 1. The amount of matter in an object is its _____. (mass, volume)

volume 2. An object's _____ is the amount of space the object takes up. (density, volume)

Density 3. _____ is the amount of matter in a certain amount of space. (Mass, Density)

Buoyancy 4. _____ is the property of matter that describes how well an object floats. (Buoyancy, Volume)

Reviewing Concepts: True or False

Write **T** (True) or **F** (False) on the line before each statement.

F   5. Volume is measured using a balance.
T   6. To compare the density of two solid objects, you need to know their masses and their volumes.
T   7. Metric rulers are used to measure length.
T   8. Magnifying glasses and hand lenses are used to observe very small objects.

Applying Strategies: Cause and Effect

Use complete sentences to answer question 9. (2 points)

9. What is the effect of placing an object with a greater density than water in a bucket of water?

Sample answer: The effect is that the object sinks in the water.

Panel 1 (top left)

Name _____

Lesson 2: How are properties of matter measured?

Before You Read Lesson 2

Read each statement below. Place a check mark in the circle to indicate whether you agree or disagree with the statement.

	Agree	Disagree
1. An object's mass is its weight.	○	✓
2. Volume is measured in liters.	✓	○
3. Objects that sink are more dense than water.	○	✓

After You Read Lesson 2

Reread each statement above. If the lesson supports your choice, place a check mark in the *Correct* circle. Then explain how the text supports your choice. If the lesson does not support your choice, place a check mark in the *Incorrect* circle. Then explain why your choice is wrong.

		Correct	Incorrect
1.	_____	○	○
2.	_____	○	○
3.	_____	○	○

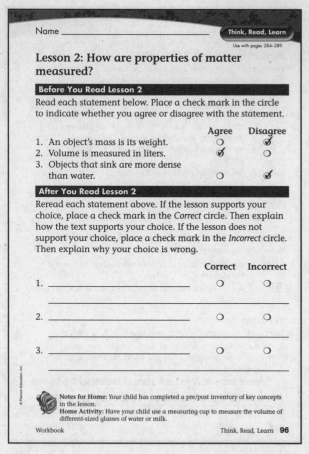

Notes for Home: Your child has completed a pre/post inventory of key concepts in the lesson.
Home Activity: Have your child use a measuring cup to measure the volume of different-sized glasses of water or milk.

Workbook   Think, Read, Learn **96**

Panel 2 (top right)

Name _____

Write the words in the diagram where they belong. Then add examples for three vocabulary words.

physical change   mixture   chemical change   solution

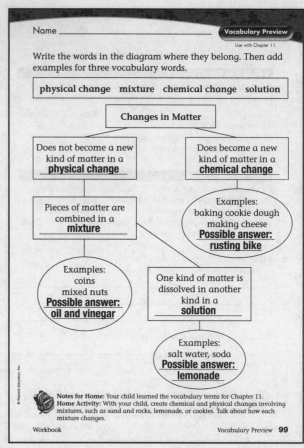

Changes in Matter

Does not become a new kind of matter in a **physical change**

Does become a new kind of matter in a **chemical change**

Pieces of matter are combined in a **mixture**

Examples: baking cookie dough making cheese **Possible answer: rusting bike**

Examples: coins mixed nuts **Possible answer: oil and vinegar**

One kind of matter is dissolved in another kind in a **solution**

Examples: salt water, soda **Possible answer: lemonade**

Notes for Home: Your child learned the vocabulary terms for Chapter 11.
Home Activity: With your child, create chemical and physical changes involving mixtures, such as sand and rocks, lemonade, or cookies. Talk about how each mixture changes.

Workbook   Vocabulary Preview **99**

Panel 3 (bottom left)

Name _____

Cause and Effect

Read the science article.

How Wood Burns

What happens to wood when it burns? It gives off heat, of course. It also goes through a chemical change. The wood combines with oxygen and changes to new substances. Some of the wood turns into gases that go into the atmosphere. Much of the wood is changed to ashes. When you put out a campfire, you are looking at a chemical change!

100 How to Read Science   Workbook

Panel 4 (bottom right)

Name _____

Apply It!

Fill in the graphic organizer. Write a cause and three effects from the article. **Answers include the following cause and multiple effects:**

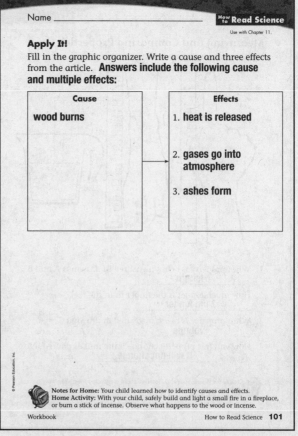

Cause	Effects
wood burns	1. heat is released
	2. gases go into atmosphere
	3. ashes form

Notes for Home: Your child learned how to identify causes and effects.
Home Activity: With your child, safely build and light a small fire in a fireplace, or burn a stick of incense. Observe what happens to the wood or incense.

Workbook   How to Read Science **101**

Name _____

Lesson 1: What are physical changes in matter?

Before You Read Lesson 1

Read each statement below. Place a check mark in the circle to indicate whether you agree or disagree with the statement.

	Agree	Disagree
1. A physical change means matter changes form.	✓	○
2. Melting is not a physical change.	○	✓
3. Ice and water contain the same particles.	✓	○

After You Read Lesson 1

Reread each statement above. If the lesson supports your choice, place a check mark in the *Correct* circle. Then explain how the text supports your choice. If the lesson does not support your choice, place a check mark in the *Incorrect* circle. Then explain why your choice is wrong.

	Correct	Incorrect
1. _____	○	○
2. _____	○	○
3. _____	○	○

Notes for Home: Your child has completed a pre/post inventory of key concepts in the lesson.
Home Activity: Have your child help make dinner. Point out physical changes, such as cutting up fruit or salting potatoes.

Workbook   Think, Read, Learn **102**

Name _____

Reviewing Terms: Matching

Match each description with the correct phrase. Write the letter on the line next to each description.

__b__ 1. when matter changes the way it looks without becoming a new kind of matter

__a__ 2. the forms that matter can take

a. states of matter
b. physical change

Reviewing Concepts: True or False

Write **T** (True) or **F** (False) on the line before each statement.

__F__ 3. After a physical change there is a new kind of matter.

__T__ 4. A change from one state of matter to another is a physical change.

__T__ 5. A change in temperature can cause a change of state.

__F__ 6. The particles in water move more when it is a solid than they do when it is a liquid.

__F__ 7. When water evaporates, it becomes a new kind of matter.

__T__ 8. When water freezes, the amount of water stays the same.

Analyzing Strategies: Cause and Effect

Use a complete sentence to answer question 9. (2 points)

9. What is the effect of placing a block of ice in the hot sunshine?
   Sample answer: The effect would be that the block of ice melts, or changes its state.

102A Lesson Review   Workbook

Name _____

Lesson 2: What are some ways to combine matter?

Before You Read Lesson 2

Read each statement below. Place a check mark in the circle to indicate whether you agree or disagree with the statement.

	Agree	Disagree
1. A mixture contains two or more kinds of matter.	✓	○
2. A solution is a kind of mixture.	✓	○
3. Solutions cannot be separated.	○	✓

After You Read Lesson 2

Reread each statement above. If the lesson supports your choice, place a check mark in the *Correct* circle. Then explain how the text supports your choice. If the lesson does not support your choice, place a check mark in the *Incorrect* circle. Then explain why your choice is wrong.

	Correct	Incorrect
1. _____	○	○
2. _____	○	○
3. _____	○	○

Notes for Home: Your child has completed a pre/post inventory of key concepts in the lesson.
Home Activity: With your child, make a mixture of sand and pebbles. Choose a method of separating the mixture. Repeat with a mixture of sand and salt.

Workbook   Think, Read, Learn **103**

Name _____

Reviewing Terms: Sentence Completion

Complete each sentence with the correct word.

__mixture__ 1. Two or more kinds of matter placed together form a _____. (gas, mixture)

__solution__ 2. A _____ is formed when one substance dissolves in another. (solution, solid)

Reviewing Concepts: Sentence Completion

Complete the sentence with the correct word or phrase.

__mixture__ 3. A pile of pennies, nickels, and dimes is a _____. (mixture, solution)

__stays the same__ 4. When a mixture is formed, each kind of matter _____. (changes, stays the same)

__magnet__ 5. A mixture of sand and small iron pieces can be separated using a _____. (strainer, magnet)

__boiling__ 6. Salt can be separated out of a salt water solution by _____. (straining, boiling)

__physical change__ 7. Dissolving is a _____. (change in state, physical change)

__stays the same__ 8. When salt dissolves in water, the amount of salt _____. (decreases, stays the same)

Applying Strategies: Calculating

9. A mixture was formed with 220 grams of marbles, 52 grams of sand, and 127 grams of iron pieces. What was the total mass of the mixture? Show your work. (2 points)

> **220 g + 52 g + 127 g = 399 g**

103A Lesson Review   Workbook

© Pearson Education, Inc.

Panel 1 (top left)

Name _____

Lesson 3: What are chemical changes in matter?

Before You Read Lesson 3

Read each statement below. Place a check mark in the circle to indicate whether you agree or disagree with the statement.

	Agree	Disagree
1. Cooking food causes chemical changes.	✓	○
2. Chemical changes always happen quickly.	○	✓
3. Digesting food is a chemical change.	✓	○

After You Read Lesson 3

Reread each statement above. If the lesson supports your choice, place a check mark in the *Correct* circle. Then explain how the text supports your choice. If the lesson does not support your choice, place a check mark in the *Incorrect* circle. Then explain why your choice is wrong.

	Correct	Incorrect
1. _____	○	○
2. _____	○	○
3. _____	○	○

Notes for Home: Your child has completed a pre/post inventory of key concepts in the lesson.
Home Activity: As you and your child read a library book, list the chemical changes that are happening in the illustrations, such as burning gasoline or cooking food.

Panel 2 (top right)

Name _____

Reviewing Terms: Sentence Completion

Complete the sentence with the correct phrase.

chemical change 1. A _____ happens when one kind of matter changes into a different kind of matter. (chemical change, physical change)

Reviewing Concepts: Matching

Some changes in matter are chemical changes. Some changes are not. For each change in matter in the left column, choose the correct description in the right column. You can use each answer more than once.

- **a** 2. baking cookie dough
- **b** 3. slicing a loaf of bread
- **a** 4. iron rusting
- **b** 5. ice melting
- **a** 6. wood burning
- **b** 7. paper tearing
- **b** 8. water evaporating

a. chemical change
b. not a chemical change

Writing

Use complete sentences to answer question 9. (2 points)

9. Write a paragraph that describes one chemical change that is a part of your everyday life.

Sample: A chemical change that is a part of my everyday life is when gasoline is burned in a car's engine. When the gasoline is burned, energy is released. I ride in a car every day, so this is a chemical change that is a part of my life.

Panel 3 (bottom left)

Name _____

A Closer Look at Mixtures

Use the pictures to answer the questions.

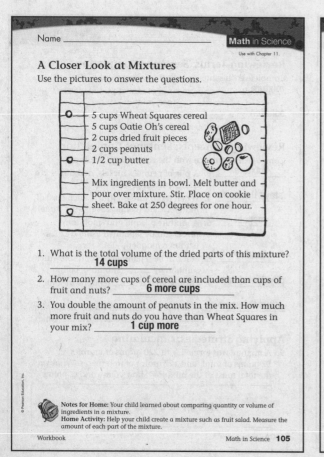

5 cups Wheat Squares cereal
5 cups Oatie Oh's cereal
2 cups dried fruit pieces
2 cups peanuts
1/2 cup butter

Mix ingredients in bowl. Melt butter and pour over mixture. Stir. Place on cookie sheet. Bake at 250 degrees for one hour.

1. What is the total volume of the dried parts of this mixture?
14 cups

2. How many more cups of cereal are included than cups of fruit and nuts? **6 more cups**

3. You double the amount of peanuts in the mix. How much more fruit and nuts do you have than Wheat Squares in your mix? **1 cup more**

Notes for Home: Your child learned about comparing quantity or volume of ingredients in a mixture.
Home Activity: Help your child create a mixture such as fruit salad. Measure the amount of each part of the mixture.

Panel 4 (bottom right)

Name _____

Write the vocabulary word that answers each riddle.

position	motion	relative position
speed	force	gravity
friction	weight	work

1. It tells the location of something. It is specific. Every place on a map has this. What is it? **position**

2. It is a force. It opposes motion. It slows moving objects. What is it? **friction**

3. It is a push or a pull. It can result from two objects coming in contact. It can also result when an object does not touch anything. What is it? **force**

4. It locates one thing in relationship to other things. It changes when direction of motion changes. What is it? **relative position**

5. It pulls objects toward each other. It is a force. It does not require contact. It increases as mass increases. What is it? **gravity**

6. You have this because of gravity. On Earth, it is about the same as mass. It decreases as you travel away from the center of Earth. What is it? **weight**

7. This tells how fast something changes position. It is a rate of change. It can be fast or slow. It can be constant or variable. What is it? **speed**

8. You do this when you move something. Machines can help you do this more easily. What is it? **work**

9. Anytime an object changes position, this is involved. When your bike rolls, this would be described as forward. When Earth rotates, this is described as circular. What is it? **motion**

Notes for Home: Your child learned the vocabulary terms for Chapter 12.
Home Activity: Ask your child to explain the vocabulary terms to you using photos, diagrams, and other graphics in the chapter to help.

ⓒ Summarize

Read the science article.

Force

Some forces can cause objects to move without touching them. The force of gravity, for example, pulls a ball that you throw back to Earth. Gravity from the Moon and the Sun tugs at the oceans and causes high and low tides. A magnet also exerts a force. It can pull a metal object to itself from inches, or even feet, away.

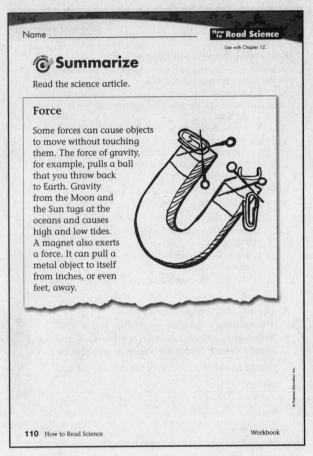

Apply It!

Fill in the graphic organizer. Write three details and a summary of the article on page 110.

Detail	Detail	Detail
gravity pulls ball to Earth	gravity from the Moon and Sun moves oceans, causing tides	magnets pull metal objects

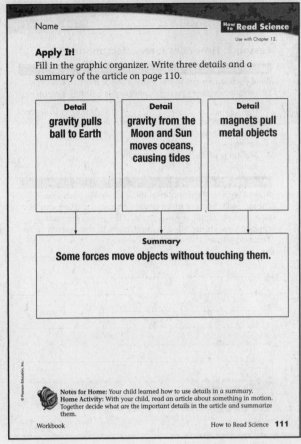

Summary

Some forces move objects without touching them.

Notes for Home: Your child learned how to use details in a summary.
Home Activity: With your child, read an article about something in motion. Together decide what are the important details in the article and summarize them.

Lesson 1: What happens when things change position?

Before You Read Lesson 1

Read each statement below. Place a check mark in the circle to indicate whether you agree or disagree with the statement.

	Agree	Disagree
1. Motion is change of position.	✓	○
2. An object with variable speed moves at the same rate.	○	✓
3. A constant speed is always fast.	○	✓

After You Read Lesson 1

Reread each statement above. If the lesson supports your choice, place a check mark in the *Correct* circle. Then explain how the text supports your choice. If the lesson does not support your choice, place a check mark in the *Incorrect* circle. Then explain why your choice is wrong.

	Correct	Incorrect
1. _____	○	○
_____		
2. _____	○	○
_____		
3. _____	○	○
_____		

Notes for Home: Your child has completed a pre/post inventory of key concepts in the lesson.
Home Activity: Have your child use toy cars or other movable objects to demonstrate slow, fast, constant, and variable speed.

Reviewing Terms: Sentence Completion

Complete each sentence with the correct word or phrase.

__relative position__ 1. An object's _____ compares its position to the position of other objects. (relative position, speed)

__motion__ 2. An object that is in _____ keeps changing position. (relative position, motion)

__position__ 3. An object's location is its _____. (position, speed)

__Speed__ 4. _____ is how fast an object changes position. (Motion, Speed)

Reviewing Concepts: True or False

Write **T** (True) or **F** (False) on the line before each statement.

__T__ 5. A map is a drawing of a place that shows the position of objects.

__T__ 6. Words like *forward*, *left*, and *right* can describe the position of an object.

__F__ 7. All objects move at the same speed.

__F__ 8. A constant speed is a speed that is always changing.

Applying Strategies: Calculating

9. If a family biked 18 kilometers in 3 hours, what was their average speed in kilometers per hour? Show your work. (2 points)

18 kilometers ÷ 3 hours = 6 kilometers per hour

Workbook   Answer Key **T31**

Use with pages 332–337.

Lesson 2: How does force affect motion?

Before You Read Lesson 2

Read each statement below. Place a check mark in the circle to indicate whether you agree or disagree with the statement.

	Agree	Disagree
1. Gravity causes you to have weight.	✓	○
2. Friction always helps objects move faster.	○	✓
3. Motion is often the result of many forces.	✓	○

After You Read Lesson 2

Reread each statement above. If the lesson supports your choice, place a check mark in the *Correct* circle. Then explain how the text supports your choice. If the lesson does not support your choice, place a check mark in the *Incorrect* circle. Then explain why your choice is wrong.

	Correct	Incorrect
1. _____	○	○
2. _____	○	○
3. _____	○	○

Notes for Home: Your child has completed a pre/post inventory of key concepts in the lesson.
Home Activity: Have your child push a toy car or other wheeled object over a wood or tiled floor, then a carpeted floor. Talk about which surface produced more friction.

Use with pages 332–337.

Reviewing Terms: Matching

Match each description with the correct word. Write the letter on the line next to each description.

__b__ 1. any push or pull

__d__ 2. a contact force that goes against motion

__c__ 3. a non-contact force that pulls all objects together and all objects toward the center of Earth

__a__ 4. a non-contact force that pulls on metals with iron in them

a. magnetism
b. force
c. gravity
d. friction

Reviewing Concepts: True or False

Write **T** (True) or **F** (False) on the line before each statement.

__T__ 5. Forces can change an object's motion.

__T__ 6. Friction can cause a moving object to slow down or to stop.

__F__ 7. Equal forces in opposite directions change an object's motion.

__T__ 8. Weight is the amount of gravity that pulls on an object.

Applying Strategies: Summarize

Use a complete sentence to answer question 9. (2 points)

9. Write a sentence that summarizes how forces affect motion.

Sample answer: Forces are pushes or pulls that can change an object's position or the direction of its motion.

Use with pages 338–343.

Lesson 3: How do simple machines affect work?

Before You Read Lesson 3

Read each statement below. Place a check mark in the circle to indicate whether you agree or disagree with the statement.

	Agree	Disagree
1. Pushing on a mountain is work.	○	✓
2. A wedge is used to split or cut.	✓	○
3. A lever rests on a support.	✓	○

After You Read Lesson 3

Reread each statement above. If the lesson supports your choice, place a check mark in the *Correct* circle. Then explain how the text supports your choice. If the lesson does not support your choice, place a check mark in the *Incorrect* circle. Then explain why your choice is wrong.

	Correct	Incorrect
1. _____	○	○
2. _____	○	○
3. _____	○	○

Notes for Home: Your child has completed a pre/post inventory of key concepts in the lesson.
Home Activity: Help your child identify an example of each simple machine among his or her toys or among household objects.

Use with pages 338–343.

Reviewing Terms: Sentence Completion

Complete the sentence with the correct word.

__Work__ 1. _____ is done when a force moves an object. (Work, Distance)

Reviewing Concepts: Sentence Completion

Complete each sentence with the correct word or phrase.

__do not__ 2. Machines _____ change the amount of work needed to do a task. (do, do not)

__inclined plane__ 3. A ramp is an example of a(n) _____. (pulley, inclined plane)

__wedge__ 4. One example of a _____ is a knife. (wedge, screw)

__screw__ 5. An inclined plane wrapped around a center post is a _____. (screw, wedge)

__lever__ 6. A seesaw is one kind of _____. (pulley, lever)

__wheel and axle__ 7. A doorknob is a(n) _____ that makes opening a door easier. (wheel and axle, inclined plane)

__pulley__ 8. You can use a _____ to change the direction of your force. (pulley, wedge)

Writing

Use complete sentences to answer question 9. (2 points)

9. Write a paragraph that tells about a time when you used a simple machine to make work easier.

Sample answer: At dinner last night I used a knife. A knife is a wedge, which is a simple machine. It made cutting my food easier.

© Pearson Education, Inc.

T32 Answer Key   Workbook

Relating Speed, Distance, and Time

Use the formulas to solve the word problems.

$$\text{Distance} = \text{Time} \times \text{Speed}$$

$$\text{Time} = \frac{\text{Distance}}{\text{Speed}}$$

$$\text{Speed} = \frac{\text{Distance}}{\text{Time}}$$

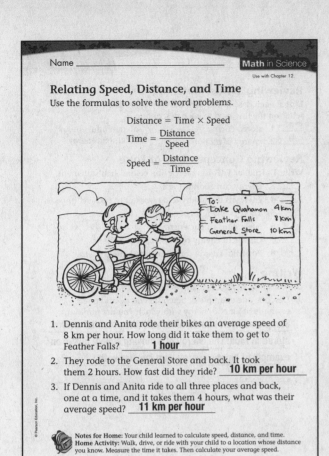

To:
Lake Quahanon 4 km
Feather Falls 8 km
General Store 10 km

1. Dennis and Anita rode their bikes an average speed of 8 km per hour. How long did it take them to get to Feather Falls? ____**1 hour**____

2. They rode to the General Store and back. It took them 2 hours. How fast did they ride? __**10 km per hour**__

3. If Dennis and Anita ride to all three places and back, one at a time, and it takes them 4 hours, what was their average speed? __**11 km per hour**__

Notes for Home: Your child learned to calculate speed, distance, and time.
Home Activity: Walk, drive, or ride with your child to a location whose distance you know. Measure the time it takes. Then calculate your average speed.

Write the words in the blanks.

potential energy	kinetic energy	thermal energy
reflect	refract	absorb
electric charge	electric current	electric circuit

A. Kinds of Energy

potential energy (stored)	**kinetic energy** (moving objects)	**thermal energy** (produces heat)	Chemical energy	Electrical energy	Light energy

B. Light Energy—It moves in a straight line until it hits an object.
Light can ___**reflect**___ or bounce. It can ___**refract**___ or bend. It can be ___**absorbed**___ or soak in.

C. Electricity
Particles of matter have an ___**electric charge**___. An ___**electric current**___ causes the bulb to light. Electricity flows through an ___**electric circuit**___.

Notes for Home: Your child learned the vocabulary terms for Chapter 13.
Home Activity: Ask your child to explain the vocabulary terms to you, using the diagrams and illustrations in their text.

Main Idea and Supporting Details

Read the science article.

Energy in Motion

Energy is always in motion. Look around you and you will see many examples. A bike racing downhill carries energy. Energy moves through wires as electric current. Heat energy moves from a warm object to a cooler object.

Apply It!

Write the main idea of the science article in the box on the next page. Then write details that support the main idea in the circles.

Main Idea
Energy is always in motion.

Supporting Details
A moving bike carries energy.

Supporting Details
Electric energy travels through wires.

Supporting Details
Heat energy moves from a hot object to a cool object.

Notes for Home: Your child learned how to identify main ideas and supporting details.
Home Activity: With your child, find and read an article in a magazine. Ask your child to find the main idea of a paragraph in the article and point out supporting details.

Use with pages 359–361.

Lesson 1: What is energy?

Before You Read Lesson 1

Read each statement below. Place a check mark in the circle to indicate whether you agree or disagree with the statement.

	Agree	Disagree
1. The Sun gives us heat and light energy.	✓	○
2. A pile of coal has potential energy.	✓	○
3. A car in the garage has kinetic energy.	○	✓

After You Read Lesson 1

Reread each statement above. If the lesson supports your choice, place a check mark in the *Correct* circle. Then explain how the text supports your choice. If the lesson does not support your choice, place a check mark in the *Incorrect* circle. Then explain why your choice is wrong.

	Correct	Incorrect
1. _____	○	○
2. _____	○	○
3. _____	○	○

Notes for Home: Your child has completed a pre/post inventory of key concepts in the lesson.
Home Activity: Have your child help you make a snack. Talk about the forms of potential and kinetic energy involved in the task. Discuss how your body uses the energy.

Workbook   Think, Read, Learn **122**

Use with pages 359–361.

Reviewing Terms: Matching

Match each description with the correct phrase. Write the letter on the line next to each description.

__a__ 1. stored energy   a. potential energy
__b__ 2. energy of motion   b. kinetic energy

Reviewing Concepts: True or False

Write **T** (True) or **F** (False) on the line before each statement.

__T__ 3. Energy can change form.
__T__ 4. Energy is the ability to do work or to cause change.
__F__ 5. There is one form of energy.
__F__ 6. Fuels store kinetic energy.
__T__ 7. Chemical energy can be stored in batteries.
__T__ 8. Potential energy can change to kinetic energy.

Writing

Use complete sentences to answer question 9. (2 points)

9. Describe one example of potential energy and one example of kinetic energy with which you are familiar.

Sample answer: I am familiar with the potential energy stored in food. The energy of a moving school bus is an example of kinetic energy I am familiar with.

122A Lesson Review   Workbook

Use with pages 366–369.

Lesson 3: What is heat energy?

Before You Read Lesson 3

Read each statement below. Place a check mark in the circle to indicate whether you agree or disagree with the statement.

	Agree	Disagree
1. Thermal energy comes from the motion of particles.	✓	○
2. Heat travels from cooler to warmer matter.	○	✓
3. Heat can change the state of matter.	✓	○

After You Read Lesson 3

Reread each statement above. If the lesson supports your choice, place a check mark in the *Correct* circle. Then explain how the text supports your choice. If the lesson does not support your choice, place a check mark in the *Incorrect* circle. Then explain why your choice is wrong.

	Correct	Incorrect
1. _____	○	○
2. _____	○	○
3. _____	○	○

Notes for Home: Your child has completed a pre/post inventory of key concepts in the lesson.
Home Activity: With your child, make juice pops in an ice tray. Discuss why heat moved from the liquid juice into the freezer and what changed because of the loss.

Workbook   Think, Read, Learn **123**

Use with pages 362–365.

Reviewing Concepts: Sentence Completion

Complete each sentence with the correct word.

__chemical__ 1. Your body uses the _____ energy in food. (electrical, chemical)
__heat__ 2. When energy changes form, some energy is always given off as _____. (heat, light)
__mechanical__ 3. The energy in moving objects is _____ energy. (thermal, mechanical)
__electrical__ 4. The appliances in people's homes are powered by _____ energy. (electrical, light)
__light__ 5. Plants use _____ energy from the Sun to make food. (chemical, light)
__energy__ 6. Waves carry _____. (water, energy)
__lose__ 7. As waves move away from their source, they _____ energy. (gain, lose)
__wide__ 8. Waves that are _____ have lots of energy. (wide, narrow)

Writing

Use complete sentences to answer question 9. (2 points)

9. Write a paragraph that describes energy changing from one form to another.

Sample answer: The Sun's energy travels to Earth as light. It is changed by plants into chemical energy. That chemical energy is in the foods we eat.

123A Lesson Review   Workbook

T34 Answer Key   Workbook

Lesson 2: How does energy change form?

Before You Read Lesson 2

Read each statement below. Place a check mark in the circle to indicate whether you agree or disagree with the statement.

	Agree	Disagree
1. A carrot holds chemical energy.	✓	○
2. Electrical charges give off heat.	○	✓
3. Energy is often useful when it is changing form.	✓	○

After You Read Lesson 2

Reread each statement above. If the lesson supports your choice, place a check mark in the *Correct* circle. Then explain how the text supports your choice. If the lesson does not support your choice, place a check mark in the *Incorrect* circle. Then explain why your choice is wrong.

	Correct	Incorrect
1. _____	○	○
2. _____	○	○
3. _____	○	○

Notes for Home: Your child has completed a pre/post inventory of key concepts in the lesson.
Home Activity: With your child, make waves using a spiral wire toy. Identify the trough and crest. Note how the waves change as you add more energy with your arms.

© Pearson Education, Inc.

Reviewing Terms: Sentence Completion

Complete the sentence with the correct phrase.

thermal energy 1. The energy of moving particles is _____. (thermal energy, electrical energy)

Reviewing Concepts: True or False

Write **T** (True) or **F** (False) on the line before each statement.

__T__ 2. Thermal energy travels as heat.

__F__ 3. Heat moves from cooler objects to warmer objects.

__T__ 4. When energy changes form, some heat is given off.

__T__ 5. The change from ice to liquid water is related to a change in energy.

__T__ 6. Friction caused by rubbing gives off heat.

__T__ 7. Heat can cause water to evaporate.

__F__ 8. Liquid water boils as it turns to ice.

Applying Strategies: Calculating

9. On the Fahrenheit scale, water boils at 212 degrees and freezes at 32 degrees. What is the difference between these two temperatures? Show your work. (2 points)

$$212 - 32 = 180 \text{ degree difference}$$

© Pearson Education, Inc.

Lesson 4: What is light energy?

Before You Read Lesson 4

Read each statement below. Place a check mark in the circle to indicate whether you agree or disagree with the statement.

	Agree	Disagree
1. Only the Sun and chemical changes produce light.	○	✓
2. Reflected light bounces off a smooth surface.	✓	○
3. Color results from refracted light.	○	✓

After You Read Lesson 4

Reread each statement above. If the lesson supports your choice, place a check mark in the *Correct* circle. Then explain how the text supports your choice. If the lesson does not support your choice, place a check mark in the *Incorrect* circle. Then explain why your choice is wrong.

	Correct	Incorrect
1. _____	○	○
2. _____	○	○
3. _____	○	○

Notes for Home: Your child has completed a pre/post inventory of key concepts in the lesson.
Home Activity: With your child, place a black cloth and a white cloth in sunlight. Discuss why the black cloth absorbs more heat than the white cloth.

© Pearson Education, Inc.

Reviewing Terms: Matching

Match each description with the correct word or phrase. Write the letter on the line next to each description.

__b__ 1. light bouncing off an object   a. absorb

__c__ 2. light bending   b. reflect

__a__ 3. light being taken in by an object   c. refract

Reviewing Concepts: Sentence Completion

Complete each sentence with the correct word or phrase.

Light 4. _____ is energy that can be seen. (Light, Heat)

electrical energy 5. Light bulbs use _____ to make light. (electrical energy, chemical energy)

straight lines 6. Light travels from its source in _____. (straight lines, curved lines)

angle 7. The length of a shadow depends on the _____ of the light. (brightness, angle)

many 8. Light is made up of _____ colors. (one, many)

Applying Strategies: Main Idea and Supporting Details

Use complete sentences to answer question 9. (2 points)

9. List three details that support the main idea below.

Main Idea: Objects can reflect, refract, or absorb light.

Detail: **Shiny, smooth objects reflect light well.**

Detail: **The lenses in people's eyes refract light.**

Detail: **A green object absorbs all colors of light except green.**

© Pearson Education, Inc.

Name

Lesson 5: What is electrical energy?

Before You Read Lesson 5

Read each statement below. Place a check mark in the circle to indicate whether you agree or disagree with the statement.

	Agree	Disagree
1. Lightning is a kind of electric circuit.	○	☑
2. Electric energy can be changed to sound energy.	☑	○
3. An open switch breaks an electric circuit.	☑	○

After You Read Lesson 5

Reread each statement above. If the lesson supports your choice, place a check mark in the *Correct* circle. Then explain how the text supports your choice. If the lesson does not support your choice, place a check mark in the *Incorrect* circle. Then explain why your choice is wrong.

	Correct	Incorrect
1. _____	○	○
_____		
2. _____	○	○
_____		
3. _____	○	○

Notes for Home: Your child has completed a pre/post inventory of key concepts in the lesson.
Home Activity: With your child, list appliances in your home that use electricity. Make a chart to sort the appliances into those used to produce light, heat, and sound.

Name

Reviewing Terms: Matching

Match each description with the correct phrase. Write the letter on the line next to each description.

__b__ 1. a tiny amount of energy, this can be positive or negative

__c__ 2. movement of electrical energy or electrical charge

__a__ 3. the path through which an electric current flows

a. electric circuit
b. electric charge
c. electric current

Reviewing Concepts: True or False

Write **T** (True) or **F** (False) on the line before each statement.

__T__ 4. Particles balance each other when they have an equal number of positive and negative charges.

__F__ 5. Two objects with negative charges will attract each other.

__T__ 6. Lightning is an uncontrolled electric current.

__F__ 7. When the switch in an electric circuit is open, current can flow.

__T__ 8. Electrical energy is changed to sound energy in a radio speaker.

Applying Strategies: Compare and Contrast

Use complete sentences to answer question 9. (2 points)

9. Describe one similarity and one difference between the electricity in lightning and the electricity in an electrical circuit.

A similarity is that both of these are moving electricity.

A difference is that the electricity in an electrical circuit is controlled, while the electricity in lightning is uncontrolled.

Name

Measuring Temperature

Mickie used the thermometer below to measure the temperatures of tap water and bath water.

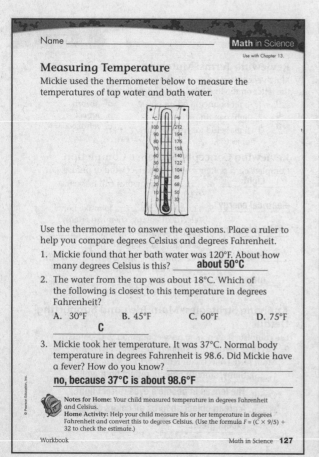

Use the thermometer to answer the questions. Place a ruler to help you compare degrees Celsius and degrees Fahrenheit.

1. Mickie found that her bath water was 120°F. About how many degrees Celsius is this? _____ **about 50°C** _____

2. The water from the tap was about 18°C. Which of the following is closest to this temperature in degrees Fahrenheit?

A. 30°F   B. 45°F   C. 60°F   D. 75°F
   C

3. Mickie took her temperature. It was 37°C. Normal body temperature in degrees Fahrenheit is 98.6. Did Mickie have a fever? How do you know? _____

   no, because 37°C is about 98.6°F

Notes for Home: Your child measured temperature in degrees Fahrenheit and Celsius.
Home Activity: Help your child measure his or her temperature in degrees Fahrenheit and convert this to degrees Celsius. (Use the formula $F = (C \times 9/5) + 32$ to check the estimate.)

Name

Write a vocabulary term from the word bank to complete each sentence. Underline the clues that helped you decide which vocabulary term to write.

pitch	vibration	compression wave

1. Energy causes <u>particles</u> of matter to <u>move back and forth</u>. It is this _____ **vibration** _____ that <u>produces sound</u>.

2. Wave motion involves <u>passing energy through particles</u>. <u>Some</u> particles are <u>squeezed together</u> while <u>others</u> are <u>spread apart</u>. This is called a _____ **compression wave**

3. A bass string <u>vibrates slowly</u> and produces a <u>low sound</u>. A violin string <u>vibrates quickly</u> and produces a <u>high sound</u>. This is a difference in _____ **pitch** _____.

Explain what is happening in the picture. Write three sentences. Use a vocabulary word in each sentence.

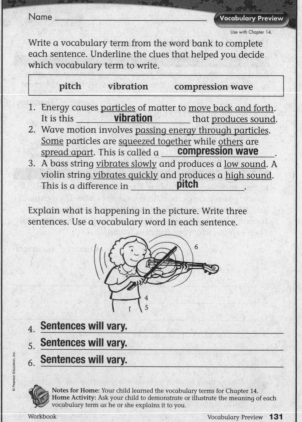

4. **Sentences will vary.**
5. **Sentences will vary.**
6. **Sentences will vary.**

Notes for Home: Your child learned the vocabulary terms for Chapter 14.
Home Activity: Ask your child to demonstrate or illustrate the meaning of each vocabulary term as he or she explains it to you.

Compare and Contrast

Read the paragraph.

Musical Instruments

A trombone and a bassoon are both wind instruments. This means they make sounds when you cause the air in them to vibrate. A trombonist vibrates his or her lips and blows into the trombone mouthpiece. This makes the air inside the instrument vibrate. A bassoonist blows on a reed, or a thin piece of wood. This makes the air in the bassoon vibrate.

Apply It!

Fill in the graphic organizer. Write ways the trombone and the bassoon are alike and ways they are different.

Trombone
Different

vibrate lips and blow into mouthpiece

Both
Alike

wind instruments, vibrate air inside instrument

Bassoon
Different

vibrate reed by blowing on it

Notes for Home: Your child learned how to compare and contrast objects.
Home Activity: With your child, listen to a recording of music. Identify several instruments. Discuss how their sounds are different and how they might be produced.

Lesson 1: What causes sounds?

Before You Read Lesson 1

Read each statement below. Place a check mark in the circle to indicate whether you agree or disagree with the statement.

	Agree	Disagree
1. When you speak, your vocal chords vibrate.	✓	○
2. Pitch is loudness or softness of sound.	○	✓
3. Short, thin harp strings make high sounds.	✓	○

After You Read Lesson 1

Reread each statement above. If the lesson supports your choice, place a check mark in the *Correct* circle. Then explain how the text supports your choice. If the lesson does not support your choice, place a check mark in the *Incorrect* circle. Then explain why your choice is wrong.

	Correct	Incorrect
1. _____	○	○
2. _____	○	○
3. _____	○	○

Notes for Home: Your child has completed a pre/post inventory of key concepts in the lesson.
Home Activity: Have your child experiment with pitch and loudness by strumming stretched rubber bands with a finger and tapping glasses with a spoon.

Reviewing Terms: Matching

Match each description with the correct word or phrase. Write the letter on the line next to each description.

__b__ 1. a back-and-forth motion   a. pitch

__a__ 2. how high or low a sound is   b. vibration

Reviewing Concepts: Sentence Completion

Complete each sentence with the correct word.

__Sound__ 3. _____ only happens when matter vibrates. (Sound, Light)

__low__ 4. Objects that vibrate slowly make a sound with a _____ pitch. (high, low)

__loudness__ 5. The _____ of sound depends on the strength of the vibrations. (pitch, loudness)

__louder__ 6. The harder you hit a drum, the _____ the sound. (louder, higher)

__air__ 7. Wind instruments make sounds when _____ inside them vibrate. (string, air)

__speak__ 8. When people _____, their vocal chords vibrate. (speak, hear)

Applying Strategies: Compare and Contrast

Use complete sentences to answer question 9. (2 points)

9. Name one similarity and one difference between *pitch* and *loudness*.

Pitch and loudness both describe sound. Pitch describes how high or low a sound is. Loudness tells the volume of a sound.

© Pearson Education, Inc.

Comparing Speeds of Sound

Compare the speeds at which sound travels through the materials in the table. Use the data to answer the questions.

Materials	Speed (Meters Per Second)
Rubber	60
Cork	500
Lead	1,210
Water at 25° Celsius	1,496
Sea water at 25° Celsius	1,531
Brick	3,650
Glass	4,540
Aluminum	5,000
Stone	5,971

1. What solids carry sound slower than water carries it?
   rubber, cork, lead

2. Does sound travel faster through fresh water or salt water? **salt water**

3. Suppose an earthquake occurs in the ocean floor. What different materials will its sound travel through? How fast will it travel through each material? **It will travel through stone at a speed of 5,971 m/sec and through sea water at a speed of 1,531 m/sec.**

Notes for Home: Your child compared the speeds at which sound travels through different materials.
Home Activity: Discuss with your child how the particles of the different materials in the chart might differ and how these differences affect their ability to transmit sound waves.

Reviewing Terms: Sentence Completion

Complete the sentence with the correct word.

compression 1. Sound waves are examples of _____ waves. (compression, atmospheric)

Reviewing Concepts: True or False

Write **T** (True) or **F** (False) on the line before each statement.

T 2. Sound travels in matter.

T 3. Sound cannot travel in outer space.

F 4. Sound travels through solids, but not through liquids and gases.

F 5. Echoes are caused when sound waves are absorbed by an object.

T 6. The outer ear collects sound waves traveling in the air.

F 7. Humans and animals can all hear the same sounds.

T 8. Bats use sound to find food.

Applying Strategies: Converting Units

9. The speed of sound in steel is 5,200 meters per second. Write this speed using the unit kilometers per second. Remember that 1,000 meters = 1 kilometer. Show your work. (2 points)

> **5,200 m/sec × 1 Km/1,000 m = 5.2 Km per second**

Lesson 2: How does sound travel?

Before You Read Lesson 2

Read each statement below. Place a check mark in the circle to indicate whether you agree or disagree with the statement.

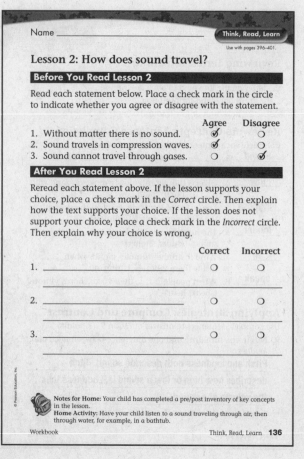

	Agree	Disagree
1. Without matter there is no sound.	✓	○
2. Sound travels in compression waves.	✓	○
3. Sound cannot travel through gases.	○	✓

After You Read Lesson 2

Reread each statement above. If the lesson supports your choice, place a check mark in the *Correct* circle. Then explain how the text supports your choice. If the lesson does not support your choice, place a check mark in the *Incorrect* circle. Then explain why your choice is wrong.

	Correct	Incorrect
1. _____	○	○
2. _____	○	○
3. _____	○	○

Notes for Home: Your child has completed a pre/post inventory of key concepts in the lesson.
Home Activity: Have your child listen to a sound traveling through air, then through water, for example, in a bathtub.

Read each sentence. Choose the answer that gives the best meaning for the boldface word.

1. Earth makes a complete **rotation** every twenty-four hours.
   A. circle   B. spin   C. day   D. week

2. The Sun is a **star** that gives Earth heat and light.
   A. super-sized planet   C. very distant object
   B. huge rock   D. hot ball of gases

3. A full Moon and a crescent Moon are two Moon **phases**.
   A. stages   C. craters
   B. separate parts D. copies

4. Earth spins on its **axis** like a wheel spins on an axle.
   A. east-to-west line   C. line from pole to pole
   B. flat pancake shape D. force field that pulls

5. In a year, Earth makes one **revolution** around the Sun.
   A. circle around a center   C. set of seasons
   B. trip to and from   D. change of direction

6. In a **lunar eclipse**, Earth moves between the Sun and Moon.
   A. blocking of the Sun's light
   B. Earth's shadow covering Moon
   C. blocking of the Moon by Earth
   D. Moon's shadow covering Earth

7. A **telescope** shows details of the Moon and stars.
   A. tool that magnifies   C. lighted tube
   B. tool that makes   D. darkened pipe
      things look smaller

8. Long ago, people named each **constellation** of stars.
   A. any cluster of stars   C. group of stars in a pattern
   B. quarter of the sky   D. half of the sky

Notes for Home: Your child learned the vocabulary terms for Chapter 15.
Home Activity: Ask your child to find an example or diagram in the chapter to help explain the meaning of each vocabulary word.

Name _____

◐ Sequence

Study the set of diagrams that show a pattern.

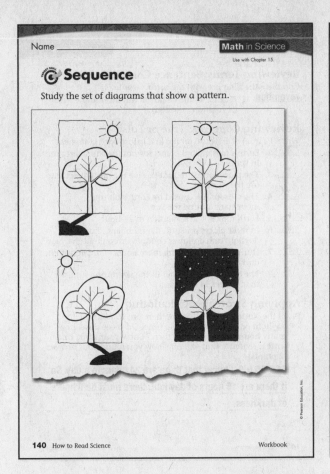

© Pearson Education, Inc.

140 How to Read Science   Workbook

Name _____

Lesson 6: How can people stay healthy?

Before You Read Lesson 6

Read each statement below. Place a check mark in the circle to indicate whether you agree or disagree with the statement.

	Agree	Disagree
1. Exercise helps the heart, lungs, and muscles.	✓	○
2. Your lungs are part of your circulatory system.	○	✓
3. Bacteria and viruses are germs.	✓	○

After You Read Lesson 6

Reread each statement above. If the lesson supports your choice, place a check mark in the *Correct* circle. Then explain how the text supports your choice. If the lesson does not support your choice, place a check mark in the *Incorrect* circle. Then explain why your choice is wrong.

	Correct	Incorrect
1. _____	○	○
2. _____	○	○
3. _____	○	○

Notes for Home: Your child has completed a pre/post inventory of key concepts in the lesson.
Home Activity: Talk with your child about a time he or she became ill. Discuss how it happened and what you did to help your child get better.

© Pearson Education, Inc.

Workbook   Think, Read, Learn **41**

Name _____

Lesson 1: What are some patterns that repeat every day?

Before You Read Lesson 1

Read each statement below. Place a check mark in the circle to indicate whether you agree or disagree with the statement.

	Agree	Disagree
1. Earth's rotation causes day and night.	✓	○
2. Earth rotates faster in winter.	○	✓
3. Shadows fall to the east in the morning.	○	✓

After You Read Lesson 1

Reread each statement above. If the lesson supports your choice, place a check mark in the *Correct* circle. Then explain how the text supports your choice. If the lesson does not support your choice, place a check mark in the *Incorrect* circle. Then explain why your choice is wrong.

	Correct	Incorrect
1. _____	○	○
2. _____	○	○
3. _____	○	○

Notes for Home: Your child has completed a pre/post inventory of key concepts in the lesson.
Home Activity: Have your child use a ball or globe to model Earth's rotation while you hold a flashlight. Discuss how rotation causes day and night.

Workbook   Think, Read, Learn **142**

© Pearson Education, Inc.

Name _____

Reviewing Terms: Matching

Match each description with the correct word. Write the letter on the line next to each description.

__b__ 1. a giant ball of hot, glowing gases
__a__ 2. the imaginary line around which Earth spins
__c__ 3. one complete spin on an axis

   a. axis
   b. star
   c. rotation

Reviewing Concepts: Sentence Completion

Complete each sentence with the correct word or phrase.

__small__ 4. Earth is _____ compared to the Sun. (large, small)

__half__ 5. At any time, _____ of Earth is facing the Sun. (half, all)

__24__ 6. Earth makes one rotation every _____ hours. (12, 24)

__change__ 7. The length and direction of shadows _____ throughout the day. (change, stay the same)

__short__ 8. Shadows are very _____ at midday. (long, short)

Applying Strategies: Sequence

9. The Sun's place in the sky seems to change throughout the day. The steps are listed below, but they are out of order. Use the clue words to place the steps in the correct order. (2 points)

Finally, the Sun appears to set in the west.
First, the Sun appears to rise in the east.
Next, the Sun appears to move across the sky.

First, the Sun appears to rise in the east.

Next, the Sun appears to move across the sky.

Finally, the Sun appears to set in the west.

© Pearson Education, Inc.

142A Lesson Review   Workbook

Workbook   Answer Key **T39**

Lesson 2: What patterns repeat every year?

Before You Read Lesson 2

Read each statement below. Place a check mark in the circle to indicate whether you agree or disagree with the statement.

	Agree	Disagree
1. A revolution is one complete spin.	○	✓
2. December is summer time in the southern half of Earth.	✓	○
3. We have less sunlight in winter.	✓	○

After You Read Lesson 2

Reread each statement above. If the lesson supports your choice, place a check mark in the *Correct* circle. Then explain how the text supports your choice. If the lesson does not support your choice, place a check mark in the *Incorrect* circle. Then explain why your choice is wrong.

	Correct	Incorrect
1. _____	○	○
2. _____	○	○
3. _____	○	○

Notes for Home: Your child has completed a pre/post inventory of key concepts in the lesson.
Home Activity: With your child, use a flashlight and a ball held at a tilted angle to model direct and indirect rays of light hitting a sphere.

Reviewing Terms: Sentence Completion

Complete the sentence with the correct word.

revolution 1. A _____ is one complete trip around the Sun. (revolution, rotation)

Reviewing Concepts: True or False

Write **T** (True) or **F** (False) on the line before each statement.

T 2. Earth's axis always points toward the same direction in space.

T 3. The places on Earth that receive the most direct Sun are the warmest.

T 4. The seasons are caused by Earth's tilt and movement around the Sun.

F 5. Earth makes one revolution in 24 hours.

T 6. In most places on Earth the number of hours of daylight and darkness changes throughout the year.

F 7. During winter there are more hours of daylight than darkness.

T 8. The Sun appears higher in the sky during summer than it does in winter.

Applying Strategies: Calculating

9. In the Northern United States there are 15 hours of daylight on some days during June. On those days, how many hours of darkness are there? Show your work, and write a sentence that explains how you found your answer. (2 points)

24 – 15 = 9. I know that there are 24 hours in a day. So if there are 15 hours of daylight, there must be 9 hours of darkness.

Lesson 3: Why does the Moon's shape change?

Before You Read Lesson 3

Read each statement below. Place a check mark in the circle to indicate whether you agree or disagree with the statement.

	Agree	Disagree
1. The Moon reflects sunlight.	✓	○
2. The Moon changes shape each month.	○	✓
3. The Moon repeats four phases each $29\frac{1}{2}$ days.	✓	○

After You Read Lesson 3

Reread each statement above. If the lesson supports your choice, place a check mark in the *Correct* circle. Then explain how the text supports your choice. If the lesson does not support your choice, place a check mark in the *Incorrect* circle. Then explain why your choice is wrong.

	Correct	Incorrect
1. _____	○	○
2. _____	○	○
3. _____	○	○

Notes for Home: Your child has completed a pre/post inventory of key concepts in the lesson.
Home Activity: With your child, observe the Moon, draw it, and identify its phase. Observe and sketch it again several days later and compare how it looks.

Reviewing Terms: Matching

Match each description with the correct word or phrase. Write the letter on the line next to each description.

b 1. each different way the Moon looks   a. lunar eclipse

a 2. when Earth blocks sunlight from reaching the Moon   b. phase

Reviewing Concepts: True or False

Write **T** (True) or **F** (False) on the line before each statement.

T 3. It takes the Moon about 29 days to complete one rotation.

F 4. The Moon makes its own light.

F 5. During a New Moon, the Moon looks like a half circle.

T 6. The Moon looks like a half circle during the First Quarter Moon.

T 7. The Full Moon looks like a circle.

F 8. The lighted half of the Moon can always be seen from Earth.

Writing

9. Write a paragraph that describes the positions of the Earth, Moon, and Sun during a lunar eclipse. (2 points)

Sample answer: During a lunar eclipse, the Earth is between the Sun and the Moon. The Earth blocks sunlight from reaching the Moon. Earth's shadow on the Moon causes the Moon to appear dark.

© Pearson Education, Inc.

Lesson 4: What are star patterns?

Before You Read Lesson 4

Read each statement below. Place a check mark in the circle to indicate whether you agree or disagree with the statement.

	Agree	Disagree
1. Stars in a constellation make a pattern.	✓	○
2. Most stars can be seen with the eyes alone.	○	✓
3. Stars are moving in space.	○	✓

After You Read Lesson 4

Reread each statement above. If the lesson supports your choice, place a check mark in the *Correct* circle. Then explain how the text supports your choice. If the lesson does not support your choice, place a check mark in the *Incorrect* circle. Then explain why your choice is wrong.

	Correct	Incorrect
1. _____	○	○
_____		
2. _____	○	○
_____		
3. _____	○	○

Notes for Home: Your child has completed a pre/post inventory of key concepts in the lesson.
Home Activity: With your child, locate an outdoor space to view stars at night. (If possible, find a location that is not brightly lit.) Look for a constellation.

Reviewing Terms: Matching

Match each description with the correct word. Write the letter on the line next to each description.

__b__ 1. a group of stars that makes a pattern

__a__ 2. a tool that magnifies faraway objects

a. telescope
b. constellation

Reviewing Concepts: True or False

Write **T** (True) or **F** (False) on the line before each statement.

__F__ 3. All stars are the same size.

__T__ 4. Some stars are brighter than others.

__T__ 5. Some telescopes use mirrors and lenses.

__F__ 6. The stars in constellations are close together in space.

__T__ 7. Stars appear to move across the sky at night.

__F__ 8. Constellations always appear in the same part of the sky.

Applying Strategies: Main Idea and Supporting Details

Use complete sentences to answer question 9. (2 points)

9. Write three details that support the main idea given below.
Main Idea: Stars appear in patterns in the sky.

Detail: **Groups of stars are called constellations.**

Detail: **Stars seem to move across the sky at night.**

Detail: **The stars in constellations are very far apart.**

Comparing Times of Moonrise and Moonset

Like the Sun, the Moon rises and sets every day. However, the time of moonrise and moonset varies more than sunrise and sunset do. Use the table below to answer the questions.

DATE	MOONRISE	MOONSET
May 9, 2004	1:00 A.M.	9:48 A.M.
July 9, 2004	12:28 A.M.	1:34 P.M.
September 9, 2004	12:55 A.M.	5:04 P.M.
November 9, 2004	2:59 A.M.	3:09 P.M.

1. How many hours and minutes were between moonrise and moonset on May 9?
8 hours, 48 minutes

2. Which date had the longest time between moonrise and moonset?
September 9, 2004

3. If you stayed up to see the Moon rise, on which date would you stay up the longest?
November 9, 2004

4. Put the dates in order, from shortest time to longest time between moonrise and moonset.
May 9, November 9, July 9, September 9

Notes for Home: Your child used a table to calculate elapsed time.
Home Activity: Study the table with your child. Decide if the Moon can only be found in the sky at night or both at night and during daylight hours.

Match each vocabulary term with its meaning. Write the letter on the blank beside it.

__b__ 1. planet

__d__ 2. asteroid

__a__ 3. orbit

__c__ 4. solar system

a. to travel in an oval path

b. a body of matter that orbits the Sun

c. the Sun, the nine planets, and their moons

d. a chunk of rock in orbit around the Sun

In the box below, draw a picture to illustrate the vocabulary terms. Use the words as labels.

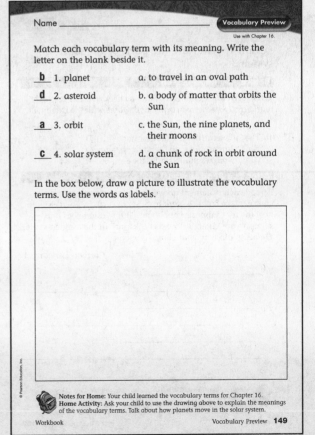

Notes for Home: Your child learned the vocabulary terms for Chapter 16.
Home Activity: Ask your child to use the drawing above to explain the meanings of the vocabulary terms. Talk about how planets move in the solar system.

Compare and Contrast

Name _____

Read the science article. Use the information to compare and contrast Mercury and Pluto.

Mercury and Pluto

Mercury and Pluto are the two smallest planets in our solar system. Both are rocky. Mercury has no atmosphere, and Pluto has almost none. But in many ways, they are different. Mercury is closest to the Sun, so it is very dry and hot. Because Pluto is farthest from the Sun, it is very cold. Mercury orbits the Sun in just 88 Earth days, but Pluto takes 248 Earth years to travel around the Sun!

Mercury   Pluto

Apply It!

In the graphic organizer on the next page, write ways the two planets are alike in the middle section. Write ways they are different on the left and the right.

150 How to Read Science   Workbook

Name _____

Use with Chapter 16.

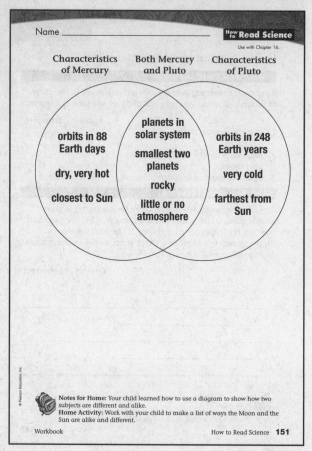

Characteristics of Mercury	Both Mercury and Pluto	Characteristics of Pluto
orbits in 88 Earth days	planets in solar system	orbits in 248 Earth years
dry, very hot	smallest two planets	very cold
closest to Sun	rocky	farthest from Sun
	little or no atmosphere	

Notes for Home: Your child learned how to use a diagram to show how two subjects are different and alike.
Home Activity: Work with your child to make a list of ways the Moon and the Sun are alike and different.

Workbook   How to Read Science 151

Name _____

Think, Read, Learn

Use with pages 455–457.

Lesson 1: What are the parts of the solar system?

Before You Read Lesson 1

Read each statement below. Place a check mark in the circle to indicate whether you agree or disagree with the statement.

	Agree	Disagree
1. The Sun is the biggest, hottest star.	○	☑
2. Nine planets make up the solar system.	○	☑
3. Gravity makes planets orbit the Sun.	☑	○

After You Read Lesson 1

Reread each statement above. If the lesson supports your choice, place a check mark in the *Correct* circle. Then explain how the text supports your choice. If the lesson does not support your choice, place a check mark in the *Incorrect* circle. Then explain why your choice is wrong.

	Correct	Incorrect
1. _____	○	○
2. _____	○	○
3. _____	○	○

Notes for Home: Your child has completed a pre/post inventory of key concepts in the lesson.
Home Activity: Ask your child to model the revolution and rotation of one of the planets in the solar system using a large ball and a small ball.

Workbook   Think, Read, Learn 152

Lesson 1 Review

Use with pages 455–457.

Reviewing Terms: Sentence Completion

Complete each sentence with the correct word or phrase.

planet 1. A(n) _____ is a large body that revolves around the Sun. (planet, asteroid)

the solar system 2. The Sun, nine planets, their moons, and other objects in orbit around the Sun make up _____. (the solar system, space)

orbit 3. An object's _____ is the path it takes around the Sun. (asteroid, orbit)

asteroids 4. Chunks of rock that orbit the Sun are called _____. (asteroids, outer planets)

Reviewing Concepts: Sentence Completion

Complete each sentence with the correct word.

star 5. The Sun is a _____. (planet, star)

gravity 6. Planets are held in orbit by the Sun's _____. (gravity, plasma)

inner 7. Mercury, Venus, Earth, and Mars are the _____ planets. (inner, outer)

Sun 8. The planets are divided into inner and outer planets based on their distance from the _____. (Moon, Sun)

Applying Strategies: Compare and Contrast

Use complete sentences to answer question 9. (2 points)

9. Name one way in which the Sun and the planets are similar. Name one way in which they are different.

Sample answer: The Sun and planets are all part of the solar system. The planets revolve, but the Sun does not.

_____

152A Lesson Review   Workbook

T42 Answer Key   Workbook

© Pearson Education, Inc.

Top-left panel

Lesson 2: What are the planets?

Before You Read Lesson 2

Read each statement below. Place a check mark in the circle to indicate whether you agree or disagree with the statement.

	Agree	Disagree
1. Mercury rotates slower than Earth.	✓	○
2. Earth's atmosphere is important to life.	✓	○
3. Jupiter and Pluto are gas giants.	○	✓

After You Read Lesson 2

Reread each statement above. If the lesson supports your choice, place a check mark in the *Correct* circle. Then explain how the text supports your choice. If the lesson does not support your choice, place a check mark in the *Incorrect* circle. Then explain why your choice is wrong.

	Correct	Incorrect
1. _____	○	○
_____		
2. _____	○	○
_____		
3. _____	○	○
_____		

Notes for Home: Your child has completed a pre/post inventory of key concepts in the lesson.
Home Activity: Make flash cards with the names of the planets. Have your child place them in order from closest to farthest from the Sun and tell about each one.

Top-right panel

Reviewing Concepts: True or False

Write **T** (True) or **F** (False) on the line before each statement.

_F_ 1. The inner planets are gas giants.
_T_ 2. Earth is the third planet from the Sun.
_T_ 3. Mars is called the "red planet."
_T_ 4. Earth can support life because of its temperature, atmosphere, and liquid water.
_F_ 5. Earth's surface always stays the same.
_F_ 6. The outer planets are much closer together than the inner planets.
_T_ 7. Gas giants have rings around them.
_T_ 8. Pluto is the smallest planet in the solar system.

Applying Strategies: Calculating

9. The distance across Earth is 12,750 kilometers. The distance across Venus is 12,000 kilometers. How much greater is the distance across Earth than the distance across Venus? Show your work. (2 points)

12,750 – 12,000 = 750 kilometers

Bottom-left panel

Finding Patterns in Tables

Every planet rotates. Some planets rotate faster than Earth, and some rotate slower than Earth. Look at the information in the table. The numbers show how many times each planet rotates for every one rotation of Earth.

Planets		Revolution Time (Earth Days)
Inner Planets	Mercury	58.8
	Venus	244
	Earth	1.0
	Mars	1.029
Outer Planets	Jupiter	0.411
	Saturn	0.428
	Uranus	0.748
	Neptune	0.802
	Pluto	0.267

1. How long does it take Venus to spin once on its axis?
244 Earth days

2. Which planet rotates fastest?
Pluto—it rotates in less than a third of an Earth day.

3. How do the inner planets compare to the outer planets in rotation?
Inner planets rotate more slowly than outer planets.

Notes for Home: Your child looked for patterns in a table.
Home Activity: With your child, search for an encyclopedia or magazine article on the solar system. Find a table comparing the planets in some way and look for a pattern.

Bottom-right panel

Match each vocabulary term with its meaning. Write the letter on the blank beside the word.

_d_ 1. technology   a. something made for the first time

_a_ 2. invention   b. machine for storing, processing, and getting information

_c_ 3. tool   c. device made by people to do work more easily

_b_ 4. computer   d. using knowledge to make tools and new ways to do things

Use each of the vocabulary terms from above to complete the diagram. Write the word that fits in the blank in each sentence.

People learn about and use their world. They use their knowledge to create **inventions**.

The **computer** is an example.

As a result, people have **technology**, which gives them new ways to do things.

This process gives them new **tools** that allow them to do work more easily.

Notes for Home: Your child learned the vocabulary terms for Chapter 17.
Home Activity: With your child, list some **tools** that make work easier, **inventions** that have changed our lives, and ways we use **technology** today.

Workbook   Answer Key **T43**

Sequence

Read the science article.

Telegraph Wire

Alexander Graham Bell knew a lot about sound and music. He wondered whether more than one message could be sent over a telegraph wire. First, he experimented to try to send signals with different pitch over one wire. Then, during his experiments, he discovered he could hear a sound over a wire. Next, he showed that a human voice could be sent through the wire. It was amazing that people could "talk with electricity"! Finally, he demonstrated the telephone by speaking to his assistant from another room.

Apply It!

Fill in the graphic organizer on the next page to show the sequence of events in Alexander Bell's invention of the telephone.

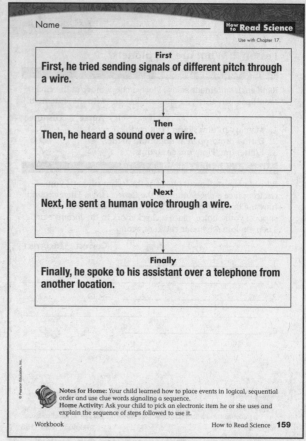

First
First, he tried sending signals of different pitch through a wire.

Then
Then, he heard a sound over a wire.

Next
Next, he sent a human voice through a wire.

Finally
Finally, he spoke to his assistant over a telephone from another location.

Notes for Home: Your child learned how to place events in logical, sequential order and use clue words signaling a sequence.
Home Activity: Ask your child to pick an electronic item he or she uses and explain the sequence of steps followed to use it.

Lesson 1: How does technology affect our lives?

Before You Read Lesson 1

Read each statement below. Place a check mark in the circle to indicate whether you agree or disagree with the statement.

	Agree	Disagree
1. People have used technology since the 1800s.	○	✓
2. Inventions improve technology.	✓	○
3. Technology systems work together.	✓	○

After You Read Lesson 1

Reread each statement above. If the lesson supports your choice, place a check mark in the *Correct* circle. Then explain how the text supports your choice. If the lesson does not support your choice, place a check mark in the *Incorrect* circle. Then explain why your choice is wrong.

	Correct	Incorrect
1. _____	○	○
2. _____	○	○
3. _____	○	○

Notes for Home: Your child has completed a pre/post inventory of key concepts in the lesson.
Home Activity: With your child, brainstorm a list of inventions that make your lives easier and more pleasant. Talk about how and why each might have been invented.

Reviewing Terms: Matching

Match each description with the correct word. Write the letter on the line next to each description.

b 1. something that helps people do work more easily

c 2. the use of knowledge to design new tools and ways of doing things

a 3. something made for the first time

a. invention
b. tool
c. technology

Reviewing Concepts: True or False

Write **T** (True) or **F** (False) on the line before each statement.

T 4. People use technology to solve problems.

F 5. Technology was not used before the year 2000.

T 6. The systems in a house work together.

T 7. Ice boxes and refrigerators are both technology.

T 8. Technology will continue to change in the future.

Writing

Use complete sentences to answer question 9. (2 points)

9. Write one or two sentences that describe an invention you have used today.

Sample answer: A microwave oven is an invention I have used today. A microwave oven cooks food more quickly than a regular oven.

Lesson 2: What are some new technologies?

Before You Read Lesson 2

Read each statement below. Place a check mark in the circle to indicate whether you agree or disagree with the statement.

	Agree	Disagree
1. GPS uses a computer to figure out location.	✓	○
2. Optical fibers improve communication.	✓	○
3. TV was invented accidentally.	○	✓

After You Read Lesson 2

Reread each statement above. If the lesson supports your choice, place a check mark in the *Correct* circle. Then explain how the text supports your choice. If the lesson does not support your choice, place a check mark in the *Incorrect* circle. Then explain why your choice is wrong.

	Correct	Incorrect
1. _____	○	○
2. _____	○	○
3. _____	○	○

Notes for Home: Your child has completed a pre/post inventory of key concepts in the lesson.
Home Activity: Ask your child to choose a technology discussed in the lesson and tell why he or she thinks it is important.

© Pearson Education, Inc.

Reviewing Terms: Sentence Completion

Complete the sentence with the correct word.

__computer__ 1. A _____ is a machine that stores, processes, and sends electronic information. (microwave, computer)

Reviewing Concepts: Sentence Completion

Complete each sentence with the correct word or phrase.

__GPS__ 2. A _____ helps navigators find their location. (GPS, microwave)

__computer chips__ 3. Calculators, cameras, and digital watches all use _____. (computer chips, satellites)

__glass__ 4. Optical fibers are made of _____. (copper, glass)

__rivers__ 5. The first transportation system used in the United States was _____. (highways, rivers)

__Planes__ 6. _____ are the fastest way to carry cargo from one place to another. (Planes, Trains)

__radiation__ 7. Microwaves are a form of _____. (radiation, radar)

__LCD__ 8. _____ is a technology that allows TV screens to be large and flat. (LCD, Glass)

Applying Strategies: Math

9. There are about one million trucks in the United States today. Write the number *one million* in standard notation. (2 points)

1,000,000

© Pearson Education, Inc.

Lesson 3: How does technology help us get energy?

Before You Read Lesson 3

Read each statement below. Place a check mark in the circle to indicate whether you agree or disagree with the statement.

	Agree	Disagree
1. Running water is needed to produce electricity.	○	✓
2. Wind and water produce most of our power.	○	✓
3. Houses can use solar power.	✓	○

After You Read Lesson 3

Reread each statement above. If the lesson supports your choice, place a check mark in the *Correct* circle. Then explain how the text supports your choice. If the lesson does not support your choice, place a check mark in the *Incorrect* circle. Then explain why your choice is wrong.

	Correct	Incorrect
1. _____	○	○
2. _____	○	○
3. _____	○	○

Notes for Home: Your child has completed a pre/post inventory of key concepts in the lesson.
Home Activity: With your child, find out how the electricity you use is produced. Discuss some ways this method affects the environment.

© Pearson Education, Inc.

Reviewing Concepts: True or False

Write **T** (True) or **F** (False) on the line before each statement.

__T__ 1. Water was used for energy before electricity was invented.

__F__ 2. Windmills and water-powered mills pollute the air and water.

__T__ 3. Wind and water are renewable resources.

__T__ 4. Hydroelectric power dams are used to make electricity.

__T__ 5. The energy in burning coal can be used to make electricity.

__F__ 6. Solar energy is the energy of wind.

__T__ 7. Windmills change the kinetic energy of wind to electricity.

__F__ 8. Through all of history, technology has been developed only in the United States.

Applying Strategies: Sequence

9. The steps of using coal to make electricity are shown below, but they are out of order. Use the clue words to write the steps in the correct order. (2 points)

Finally, pressure from steam turns wheels in electricity generators.
Next, heat is used to boil water.
First, coal is burned to produce heat.
Then boiling water makes steam.

First, coal is burned to produce heat. Next, heat is

used to boil water. Then boiling water makes steam.

Finally, pressure from steam turns wheels in electricity

generators.

© Pearson Education, Inc.

Workbook   Answer Key **T45**

Technology Time Line

In less than a hundred years, people went from the invention of the airplane to sending people into outer space. Look at the events listed in the chart. Mark each event on the time line below, then label it. The first item is done for you.

History of Flight

Year	Event
1903	First gas-powered, manned airplane flight
1926	First liquid-filled rocket launch
1958	First satellite orbits Earth
1969	First manned spacecraft lands on the Moon
1981	First flight of spacecraft that returns, lands, and can be reused
2000	First crew sent to International Space Station

first gas-powered manned airplane flight

1900   1920   1940   1960   1980   2000
1903

Notes for Home: Your child recorded events on a time line.
Home Activity: Help your child make a table showing important events in his or her life and the date they occurred. Then have your child transfer them to a time line like the one shown on this page.